JO THOMAS has lived in Dorset since 1940 and was educated at Parkstone Grammar School. She has a first class honours degree in Science and Geology from the Open University. Having assisted Paul Ensom with the recording of the palaeontology collection in the Dorset County Museum, she then recorded sites of geological interest for the Dorset Environmental Records Centre. Research on the history of quarrying resulted in an article on the lesser-known building materials in West Dorset in the *Proceedings of the Geologists' Association* and on the building stones of Dorset (parts 1-4) in the *Proceedings of the Dorset Natural History and Archaeological Society*. In partnership with Paul Ensom she compiled a *Bibliography of Dorset Geology* which was published by the Dorset Natural History and Archaeological Society in 1989. She undertook a pilot study of the use of local stone in historic buildings in Dorset on behalf of English Heritage. The Geologists' Association have given her the Foulerton Award for Services to Geology, and she is Secretary of Dorset's Important Geological Sites, a group dedicated to encouraging public understanding of the geology of Dorset. She is the author of *Stone Quarrying* in the 'Discover Dorset' series published by The Dovecote Press.

FOLLOWING PAGES
Pond House, Ashmore, built of Shaftesbury Sandstone greensand.

DOVECOTE PRESS

DORSET STONE

JO THOMAS

First published in 2008 by The Dovecote Press Ltd
Stanbridge, Wimborne Minster, Dorset BH21 4JD

ISBN 978-1-904-34963-1

Jo Thomas has asserted her rights under the Copyright, Designs
and Patent Act 1988 to be identified as author of this work

Typeset in Monotype Sabon
Printed and bound by KHL Printing, Singapore

A CIP catalogue record for this book is available
from the British Library

Contents

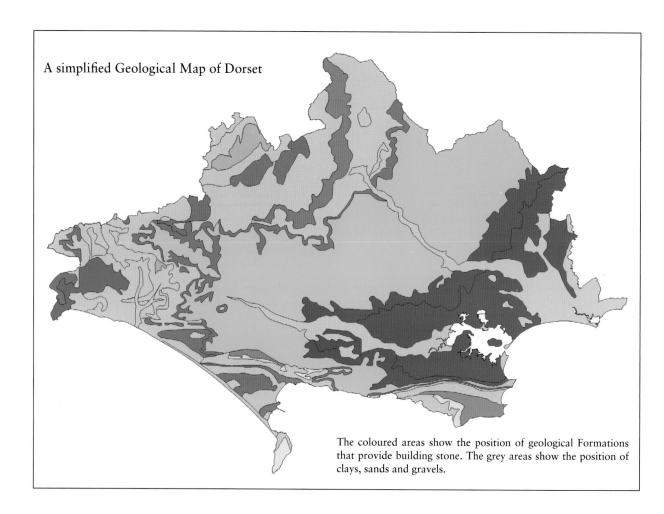

A simplified Geological Map of Dorset

The coloured areas show the position of geological Formations that provide building stone. The grey areas show the position of clays, sands and gravels.

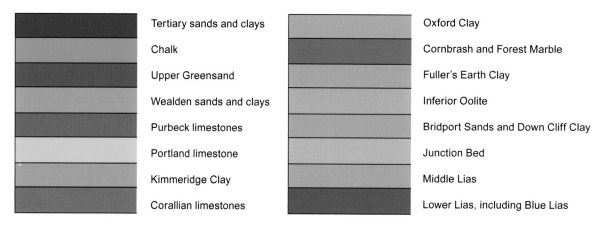

Tertiary sands and clays	Oxford Clay
Chalk	Cornbrash and Forest Marble
Upper Greensand	Fuller's Earth Clay
Wealden sands and clays	Inferior Oolite
Purbeck limestones	Bridport Sands and Down Cliff Clay
Portland limestone	Junction Bed
Kimmeridge Clay	Middle Lias
Corallian limestones	Lower Lias, including Blue Lias

CHAPTER ONE

Introduction

THE USE OF BUILDING STONE IN DORSET

Travelling around rural Dorset, the beauty of the ever-changing landscape is enhanced by the varying character of its villages. Both are the result of the diverse geology, in a repeated series of limestones, sands and clays. Until the early twentieth century local materials were used for building, and each village has a distinct character which reflects the geology of its surroundings. The majority of building stones used in the county are limestones, with lesser use of sandstone and flint (or chert). Brick and cob have made use of all the local clays.

Dorset has only a few grand houses, but many small manor houses that have grown and changed during their history. The manor houses have used the best quality stone available within their own estates, while their surrounding villages have used stone of lesser quality according to the wealth of the original builder. Agricultural buildings would have been built of anything that came to hand, and reflect the surrounding geology most closely. As the centuries went by and repairs were needed, different stone, preferably from local quarries, was used, but in most cases the source would have been within a day's journey by horse and cart.

The most famous building stones in Dorset are the Portland Freestone and the Purbeck Marble. The first has been used for many government and commercial buildings, in London and other cities throughout England. It has also been carried overseas to Dublin and even America. Purbeck Marble was carried by sea to many parts of England for interior work in churches during the twelfth to fourteenth centuries.

Quarrying activity, apart from on the Isles of Portland and Purbeck, has been on a small scale. Parish quarries have been used by the local inhabitants for repairs or new building as required, and only a few in the nineteenth century sold stone to customers up to a day's journey away. Most quarries produced roadstone as well as building stone, and lime for mortar, or for spreading on heavy clay fields.

Although it is the custom in geological literature to treat a subject stratigraphically (in the order in which rocks are laid down, with the oldest first), part of the fascination of building stones is in the way different rocks are mixed in the same building. This may be in the first place because rocks of widely differing ages occur in the same area, due to unconformities (where younger rocks have been deposited, with a large gap in time, on top of much older ones). Historically, a particular stone might have been carried long distances to be used by the same group of people. For instance wealthy landowners, including medieval abbeys, brought stone from another part of their estates. Parish loyalties might have decided a choice of stone, even though a suitable stone was available in the next parish. In addition, the suitability of certain stones for particular parts of a building encouraged more widespread use in small quantities. Transport has been a key factor in the distribution of stone, brick and roofing materials.

The distinctive character of Dorset's countryside has been created not only by its geology, but also by aeons of weathering, the growth of plants, and by man's use of the land. Stone Age man cleared the forests using sharp tools made from the flint of the Chalk hills. The flint found in the Clay with Flints has proved to be the best quality, as it has not dried out as much as the flints found loose on the surface. Iron Age man discovered that stronger tools could be made from the ironstone on Hengistbury Head.

The first use of stone as a building material in Dorset is in the tombs and stone circles of the Neolithic age. The earliest traces of stone buildings are footings within the ring fortifications of Maiden Castle. The Romans who conquered the Dorset tribes built camps and villas of the local stone, some of

Above The Roman hypocaust in the Colliton villa, Dorchester, is built of Lower Purbeck limestone from the Ridgeway.

Below The Norman tower of Studland church is built of Burr limestone from the Purbeck Formation.

which survive. At Upwey, the Lower Purbeck Cypris Freestone, a fine grained white limestone containing fossil ostracods, forms the brow of a hill above the village. This limestone was an obvious choice for the Romans when it came to building their new town of Durnovaria (Dorchester) only three miles away by the River Frome. The Colliton Roman farmhouse in Dorchester is built of flint and limestone from Upwey, while the fragment of Roman wall at Top o'Town, Dorchester, also includes large flints from the local hills. Near Beaminster they built a camp on Waddon Hill using the Inferior Oolite limestone of the hill itself.

Though the Saxons built their houses mostly of wood, some fragments remain of Saxon castle and church building. The west wall of Sherborne Abbey is of Saxon origin, and both Cerne and Shaftesbury Abbeys were founded before the Norman Conquest. As proof of conquest, the Normans destroyed Saxon work as they built their own. However, the Normans' skill with stone has given Dorset the foundation of its built heritage. Many Norman and medieval abbeys and castles are now in ruins, but their remains show that local stone was used, including the Corallian Oolite at Abbotsbury, the Inferior Oolite, Forest Marble and Fullers' Earth Rock at Sherborne Castle and the Purbeck Burr (Broken Shell Limestone) ashlar and Purbeck limestone rubble at Corfe Castle.

Many ancient buildings have acted as quarries for later buildings, or for lime burning. Over the centuries most buildings have been altered, but many churches were the subject of wholesale rebuilding in the middle to late nineteenth century. Powerstock church has an entirely nineteenth century exterior, though the chancel arch and columns in the nave are Norman work. In many cases only the church towers built in the twelfth to fifteenth centuries have survived. While domestic buildings have largely retained their local character through all the changes, churches have often lost it with the importation of Portland, Purbeck or Bath limestones in the late nineteenth century.

Particular phases of domestic building have depended on the prosperity of agriculture and industry, on disasters such as the Black Death, or town fires, or wars, and on the growth of population. The dissolution of the monasteries by Henry VIII changed land ownership for ever as the church lands were sold to the King's favourites. As abbeys and monasteries were destroyed, their stone was used either for building a new house for the new owner, or for cottages in the growing villages. The prosperity of the woollen industry encouraged more building during the sixteenth and seventeenth centuries.

Thatched roofs catching alight resulted in disastrous town fires such as Beaminster (1648) and Blandford (1731), which required full scale rebuilding of the towns, the first in stone (Inferior Oolite), the second in brick.

In the eighteenth century fortunes were made from overseas trade in sugar from the West Indies, and cod from Newfoundland. At that time many existing buildings were improved with fashionable brick frontages, as well as elegant ashlar stone. In the Bridport area wars with France in the late eighteenth and early nineteenth centuries increased the market for ropes and sails, bringing greater prosperity to an already thriving industry. Both factories and workers' cottages were built to serve the industry. For instance the Pymore Mills Co. built cottages in Loders in 1858 using stone from Mangerton for the walls, and from Bothenhampton for mortar and the vault and manhole (the cellar and its external entrance). (DRO/D203/A67B). The Forest Marble limestone from Bothenhampton is so lacking in porosity as to be almost waterproof and is therefore excellent for cellar walls.

Improving agriculture in the early nineteenth century gave the farmers who owned the land the money to improve their houses, but left the agricultural labourers living in poor conditions. However, several landowners realised the need for better housing and built good quality stone and brick houses for their workers, as can be seen in building specifications in the Dorset History Centre. Some of these estate houses provide a characteristic feature of villages, but are somewhat lost in twentieth century towns. Examples can be found around Poole and Wimborne where the 'Lady Wimborne Cottages' were built of local brick, often in pairs, with a very distinctive style between 1867 and 1904. The old Cornelia Hospital in Poole (1907, long demolished) was built in the same style and named for Lady Cornelia Guest (Lady Wimborne).

The local manufacture of bricks supplied much of the building materials required in the eighteenth and nineteenth centuries and into the twentieth century. Poole, Bothenhampton, Chickerell and Gillingham were important brickmaking areas, though smaller estate brickworks existed wherever clay was available.

Until the beginning of the First World War in 1914 the vast majority of building materials, whether stone or brick, came from within Dorset. Between the Wars stone quarrying became uneconomic compared with brick and almost died out, except for activity on Portland and Purbeck. Since the end of the Second World War most of the brickworks have also closed, leaving only the specialised Swanage brickworks using the local Wealden clay. Most of the brick used in the huge programme of building since the 1960's has been imported from elsewhere.

GEOLOGICAL HISTORY

The breathtaking beauty of the Dorset coast World Heritage Site and the landscape of inland Dorset is due to the varying nature of the rocks created during 185 million years of earth history. 205 million years ago, at the beginning of the Jurassic period, the south of England was below sea level, on the edge of a very large continent that included today's North America, Europe and Asia joined together. South America and Africa were beginning to drift apart, but the open sea known as the Tethys was to the south east, between Africa and Eurasia.

During the Jurassic period, between 205 and 145 million years ago, the opening of the south Atlantic continued northwards. The shape and depth of the continental shelves changed constantly, and the sediments deposited on the floor of these shallow seas alternated between clays (in deeper water), sands (in shallower water) and limestones (in the shallowest seas). At this time the part of the earth's crust we now call southern England was about 30 north of the equator (equivalent to today's Florida), and the shallow sea was therefore much warmer than today.

As the northern continent began to split apart the Jurassic rocks were pushed from the west above sea level, and the early Cretaceous rocks were formed on land. About 110 million years ago as the north Atlantic opened, the Jurassic and early Cretaceous rocks were both folded and stretched so that large faults occurred, with blocks of crust slipping down past their neighbours by as much as 460 metres. Over about 10 million years the tilting land was worn down to a level plain. The south-easterly dip of the land that resulted in the erosion of the early Cretaceous and Jurassic rocks was greater in the west of Dorset than in the east. West of Bridport, therefore, the Lias (earliest Jurassic) rocks were exposed, whereas in Purbeck the Upper Jurassic is continuous with the early Cretaceous.

Then in the later part of the Cretaceous period sea levels rose dramatically over the continents bordering the north Atlantic, possibly because of volcanic activity on the mid-Atlantic ridge. The clay, sand and Chalk deposited then reflect the varying depths of the sea.

About 60 million years ago continental movement again pushed the land upward, and the higher levels

APPROXIMATE GEOLOGICAL PERIODS

Tertiary - Eocene 56.5 to 35.5 million years ago
Palaeocene 65 to 56.5 million years ago
Cretaceous 146 to 65 million years ago
Jurassic 205 to 146 million years ago

of the Chalk were eroded away from south west England. After about 10 million years of erosion the sea level rose again for a while and the early Tertiary pebbles, sands and clays were deposited on an irregular Chalk surface. South and east Dorset, and much of Hampshire, were then covered in land-based sediments of clay and sand deposited by several river systems between 50 and 33 million years ago.

By 25 million years ago the continent of Africa had rotated away from South America and was pushing northwards into Europe. This movement squeezed the crust to form the Alps and caused folding in southern England. The almost vertical Chalk ridge in Purbeck was created at this time, while the Weymouth anticline (an upfold), and the older faults across south west Dorset were reactivated.

Erosion continued over Dorset and none of the later Tertiary sediments are found here. Less than 2 million years ago the northern hemisphere began to get colder. Until about 15,000 years ago Ice Ages came and went over the northern part of the British Isles, but the ice never reached Dorset. However, it was subject to permafrost conditions and the freeze – thaw activity has carved the present landscape. In particular, the Chalk has been eroded away from most of west and north Dorset, leaving the Jurassic rocks uncovered. Sediments deposited during this time are the Clay with Flints that caps some of the Chalk hills, and spreads of river gravel in as many as 14 terraces lining the basins of the rivers Frome, Stour and Avon.

It is impossible to date sedimentary rocks precisely; we can only relate them one to another by the fact that the later ones are on top of the earlier ones. Geological dating depends on the minerals in volcanic rocks that have a tendency to change from one element to another over time – a 'half-life'. World-wide geological studies can therefore give us these approximate dates. Any dates given in the text should therefore be considered only as a guide.

GENERAL DESCRIPTION OF BUILDING STONES

Building stones used in Dorset are sedimentary and result from the deposition of sand, mud or lime-mud in water. The texture of the building stones is a result of the variability of their environment of deposition. In addition to the movement of continents, climates and sea levels have changed many times over millions of years. During the Jurassic and Cretaceous periods what is now the European continent was closer to the Equator than today. The water was considerably warmer and extended over the continental margins, where limestones formed by biological, biochemical and to a lesser extent organic precipitation. Limestones are defined as consisting of over 50% calcium carbonate. There may be lesser amounts acting as cement in sandstones, or as a constituent of mudstones.

Limestones are divided into three major groups, chemical, organic or detrital. Chemically precipitated limestones can be formed by the precipitation caused by evaporation of calcium carbonate from warm shallow water, or by coating sand grains, algae or small scraps of shell with layers of calcium carbonate to form ooliths. Organic limestones consist mostly of the remains of plants and animals, which had shells or skeletons of calcium carbonate.

Chalk is the purest example of an organic limestone, consisting almost entirely of the calcareous skeletons of coccoliths (a floating alga). Other organic limestones are largely made up of the shells of bivalves, gastropods, ammonites etc., or corals, algae, crinoids (small colonial animals with calcite skeletons) or foraminifera (microscopic plankton made of calcite).

Detrital limestones are made up of fragments of pre-existing limestone, or organic carbonate. The fragments are cemented together either with micrite (calcite material which has a grain size less than 0.01 millimetre) or with sparite (coarse crystalline calcite replacing micrite or filling spaces, which has a grain size more than 0.01 millimetre). This is often known as 'sparry' calcite, and gives a crystalline appearance to the rock. Shorthand words for describing limestones include:

BIOMICRITE – a limestone consisting mostly of shells (bio) with very fine calcium carbonate (micrite) surrounding the fragments.

The quarries on Waddon Hill, Stoke Abbott, produced building stone, roadstone and lime for a wide area of West Dorset from the Inferior Oolite.

BIOSPARITE – a limestone consisting mostly of shells (bio) with crystals of calcite (sparite) cementing the shells together.

Except for the Chalk, the individual limestone beds used for building are usually less than 1 metre thick. The thickest beds, such as those from the Portland Freestone, are cut as ashlar, while the thinner beds may be broken or dressed by hand. Some of them are rich in the fossil remains of ammonites, belemnites, bivalves, gastropods, brachiopods and occasionally plants. The larger fossils may create weak points in a rock which make it unsuitable for building stone. An even-textured limestone which may be cut and placed in any direction is known as a freestone.

Sandstones consist mostly of grains of silica sand, of varying sizes and degrees of roundness, from sharp-edged to completely rounded. They may have high porosity with empty pore spaces, or be cemented with calcium carbonate; iron coated finer grains (ferruginous), or even wholly cemented together with re-crystallised silica (silcrete). Glauconite, a complex mineral including iron and aluminium that indicates a marine, near-shore sea floor environment, occurs as isolated grains in the Upper Greensand and lowest Chalk beds.

Clays are the finest grained of all the rocks and have a crystal structure which forms as horizontal plates, giving them a tendency to slip when wet, but binds them together when baked as bricks or pottery.

QUARRYING

Except for Portland and Purbeck, where quarrying has been a separate industry over many centuries, quarrying activity has been on an informal basis.

When stone was required for an individual house, the residents of the parish were permitted to take stone from the parish quarry, often by an agreement between the landowner and his tenants. This was the case when a parish had suitable stone within its boundaries, though where there was no suitable stone the builders would need to purchase stone from neighbouring parishes. When work on the farm was slack between major tasks, the farmworkers would be kept busy extracting stone from the quarry. The old quarry floor would soon regenerate grass for pasture, and today the remaining quarry faces often form the boundary of a field. Once extracted the stone could then be stored to weather over the winter before being used.

Stone in situ is full of water and is soft when extracted. It hardens as it dries, and with many stones it is advisable to let the frost act on it before using it. In each case simple hand tools could extract pieces of stone taking advantage of the joints (vertical breaks) and bedding planes (horizontal divisions) to lever out the blocks. Any soft clay on the bedding planes could be picked out with a pick-axe and then a bar could be pushed under the block and manpower used to lever it out.

At Gannets Quarry near Todber Mr. Warren, the farmer who was also a quarryman, remembers that in the 1930's an 8 foot bar could be used to lift 10 tons of stone as long as there were enough men to lean on the bar! In Durlston Bay, the thicker beds of shale between the limestones could be removed

The quarry at Winspit in Worth Matravers provided Portland Freestone until the early 20th century.

leaving a wider space. The block would then fall out under its own weight and the good stone collected from the beach.

Throughout Dorset the limestones and sandstones have resisted weathering sufficiently to now form the capping of many hills. Quarrying could therefore be undertaken into the sides of these caps, working gradually across the top of the hill in open workings. This method can be seen from the A35 Bridport by-pass on Sloes Hill, Symondsbury. Where good building stone was visible on the surface, but was covered by other less useful beds or clay as the stone dipped into the hill, the stone would be followed into the hillside in adits, as was done on Green Hill, Chalbury, and extensively in the Isle of Purbeck. This could only be achieved if the stone above the building stone was strong enough to stay in place without falling during the length of time the quarrying was continued. If it was not safe to work in adits, quarrying would stop at the point where the clay or useless stone above became too thick to make the work worthwhile. This overburden and the stone too broken to be used were placed behind the workings in spoil heaps, which today provide the only present-day clue to the presence of old quarries.

In the text, no O.S. references are given for those quarries that are within private land and have no public access.

There are a few account books from the nineteenth century that record sales of stone from particular quarries. These are described in the separate chapters on particular stones. Quarrying in Portland and Purbeck will also be described in the relevant chapter.

TRANSPORT

Up to the middle of the nineteenth century the transport of stone depended on horse and cart. A day's journey was therefore the greatest distance from a quarry that most stone would be used, except for the more commercially valuable Portland and Purbeck limestones. The majority of Dorset's rivers are too small or shallow for waterborne transport, except perhaps for the lower reaches of the Stour, though the river valleys provided an easy land route. Stone was carried on low wagons drawn by teams of horses or oxen for heavy loads.

Purbeck and Portland limestones were quarried on or near the coast and could therefore be carried around the coastline by ship and up any navigable river.

Between the twelfth and fourteenth centuries Purbeck Marble was carried on sleds from the quarries south of Corfe Castle to workshops in the town, and then across the heath to Ower Quay on the southern shore of Poole Harbour. The Marble and other limestones were taken by barge across to the quayside at Poole for transhipment into larger vessels. It could then be taken around the coast to Christchurch Harbour for use in the Priory, up the Stour as far as Wimborne, or east along the coast and up the Thames. This method of export continued up to the sixteenth century. As the use of the other Purbeck limestones, quarried near Swanage, became more important, export by ship was from Swanage. Stone and slate from Devon, Cornwall, the Isle of Wight and France has been brought into Dorset's coastal towns in similar manner for many centuries.

The Portland Freestone was quarried from cliff quarries in the Isle of Purbeck and could therefore be carried by ship, though the exposed nature of the coast made this a difficult operation. The stone was cut and then stored on the floor of the quarry until the weather was fine enough for a ship to come close to the cliff. The stone was then lifted into the ship by a crane, or 'whin'. Grooves probably cut by sledges can still be seen at low tide on the rocks below Winspit Quarry (named after the 'whin').

When Wren decided to use Portland stone for rebuilding St. Paul's Cathedral in London, a quay was built on the east side of the Isle of Portland and from then on the stone could be exported not only around England but also to Ireland, America and later to India and Australia.

In the latter half of the nineteenth century the railways provided transport for stone, bricks and slate to be carried over greater distances. From then on the variety of stone used in building churches or prestigious houses increased. During the twentieth century, as the railways declined, transport by road has increased.

MASONRY

It is the custom among architects to refer to masonry as either ashlar or rubble. While the term ashlar refers to square hewn stone used with the minimum of mortar, the term rubble seems to me to undervalue the skill of the stonemasons. While some roughly broken pieces of stone used to fill the space between the two skins of a wall may fairly be described as rubble, the vast majority of stonework has been

Above Cranes, known as whins, lifted the stone from the quarry into ships.

Below The 16th century barn at Childhay Manor was built with ashlar blocks of Inferior Oolite from Grange Quarry in Burstock.

Below Thin blocks of stone are cut with a guillotine in Landers Quarry, Acton.

dressed. Initially the stone may be roughly broken with a guillotine or long handled hammer and chisel, but further skilled work with an adze is required to arrive at neat edges, or at the very least a smooth face.

Masons usually lay stone in the same orientation as

Ham Hill Stone face-bedded in an old school in Penny Lane, Sturminster Newton, is weathering badly and spalling.

it was in its natural state, but occasionally it is used 'out of bed' with the horizontal beds of stone placed vertically. Cornices and cills are traditionally edge bedded. Similarly, arches are edge bedded in order to transfer the load correctly.

Face bedding may be successful with certain freestones, such as those in Portland, and the Freestone bed in Purbeck, but in other cases results in frost and rain attacking the fabric of the stone so that it spalls away. An example of this may be seen in Sturminster Newton, where a nineteenth century schoolhouse in Penny Lane has a wall facing the road built of Ham Hill Stone placed vertically. Layers of shelly limestone are falling away in a most alarming manner. It is possible that the action of rainwater here may be further aggravated by the proximity to exhaust fumes from cars.

Another problem with masonry that has arisen in more recent times is that cement has been used instead of lime mortar. 'Lime' was made by burning the limestone with wood, at $1000 - 1200°$ F, to drive off carbon dioxide, leaving CaO or quicklime. When water is added this becomes calcium hydroxide and when mixed with sand is used as mortar. Lime mortar is a porous, flexible material which will allow moisture within a wall to evaporate. It will also accommodate small movements within the building without cracking. When changes of temperature create tiny cracks, water within the lime mortar will dissolve the lime and reseal the cracks as if re-making limestone. The last working limekiln was in Shillingstone Chalk pit (ST824098) where lime was made in the traditional manner until the 1990's.

Most limestone quarries had a limekiln and many can still be seen. For instance the limekiln at Charmouth cement factory, now the study centre (SY364930), has been carefully preserved so that we can see the Blue Lias cobbles from which it was built. Similarly the limekiln at Wanderwell Quarry (SY470915) built of the Forest Marble, can be seen at the foot of the steps down from Coopers Drive. The owners of Bell Cottage in Loders have preserved their limekiln (Inferior Oolite) at SY498949 by covering it with a tin roof. The limekiln at Poxwell Q uarry (SY743835) is covered in ivy, but the Purbeck limestone walls are otherwise in good condition and would definitely be worth preserving.

Cement is made with limestone and clay, burnt at $1400°$ F. Containing sodium and calcium aluminium silicates, this forms interlocking crystals, will set when wet and is impervious. The hard cement will not allow evaporation, so that salts and moisture remain in the stone and are drawn out through the surface. An example of the extreme weathering caused by the use of cement based hard mortar can be seen in a garden wall on the road through the village of Marnhull, near the entrance to Love Lane.

The survival of so many stone buildings from the past nine centuries is a measure of the quality of the stone used. The quality of a particular stone, and its individual characteristics in porosity, hardness and bed height, has governed its use in particular parts of a building, or the distance that it may have been worthwhile to carry it.

The thickness of the bed, or bed height, will govern how it is used. Beds of approximately 1 metre thick can be cut as ashlar; those approximately 25 cm thick would be cut as dressed stone. Rough pieces, especially those without flat bedding planes top and bottom are used as rubble. Thin beds, or beds that split into thin slabs on the bedding planes, are used as paving or roofing.

Porosity and hardness will govern the use of stone as foundation courses or for bridges. The least porous will be used for foundations where more porous stone forms the walls. For bridges hardness is more important, as the structure must withstand the force of the water.

PREVIOUS STUDIES

Published sources on the use of building materials include Hutchins' *History of Dorset* (1774 and 1861-73), the *Victoria County History* (1908), contemporary newspaper articles, the Royal

Commission for Historical Monuments (RCHM), and the works of architectural historians. In this book the author aims to give more detail, to provide illustrations of each rock type, and descriptions of its appearance which will enable the non-geologist to identify the stone used in a particular building.

During the nineteenth and twentieth centuries both historians and geologists have studied the building stone produced in Dorset and many newspaper articles have paragraphs about particular buildings. The earliest note found by volunteers working on the bibliography of Dorset geology is 'An account of some experiments on the flexibility and strength of stones.' written by T. Tredgold for the *Philosophical Magazine* in 1820. The next is in the *Salisbury and Winchester Journal* of 13th July 1829, when it was reported that a pillar of Purbeck stone was erected to the Earl of Eldon, above Encombe House.

The 1837 meeting of the British Association for the Advancement of Science included a paper by W.B. Clarke 'On the phenomena exhibited by the plastic clay formation in the vicinity of Poole, Dorset.' At that time the clays around Poole were being increasingly used for brickmaking.

In 1840 a report for the Royal Institute of British Architects (129) was written by C.H. Smith on the 'Lithology, or observations on stone used for building (Portland).'

In 1848 a memoir of the Geological Survey of the United Kingdom by T. Ransome and B. Cooper, was written 'On the composition of some of the limestones used for building purposes, especially on those employed in the erection of the new Houses of Parliament'. This included Portland Stone, although a stone from the Midlands was eventually chosen. It was not a good choice as the magnesian limestones from Bolsover Moor, Anston and Mansfield Woodhouse in Nottinghamshire have not proved as durable as Portland in the smoky atmosphere of London.

In 1863 The Corps of Royal Engineers produced a paper 'Memorandum of the results of experiments into the comparative qualities and fitness for building purposes of samples of stone from different quarries in the Island of Portland'.

Travellers' tales from the seventeenth and eighteenth centuries included notes on the buildings. In 1888 J.J. Cartwright edited *The Travels through England of Dr. Richard Pococks* for the Camden Society. Dr. Pococks is quoted as saying that Eastbury was "Built chiefly of Melbury stone, 6 miles to the north; the ornaments are of Portland stone. [Eastbury, in Tarrant Gunville, was designed and built by Vanbrugh, being completed in 1738.] It is said the carriage of the materials cost £20,000 and the whole not less than £200,000." Recent excavations have shown that Melbury stone is a greensand similar to the older Shaftesbury Sandstone of the Upper Greensand. N.M. Richardson published the earlier travels of Peter Mundy in Dorset in 1635 in the *Proceedings of the Dorset Natural History and Archaeological Society* in 1922.

During the twentieth century the first (1910) major reference work on the geology of building stones was written by John Allen Howe, the curator and librarian at the Geological Society. At that time stone was still a major building material, though the loss of life in the 1914-18 war meant that many skilled men were lost to the quarrying industry. He describes the appearance and qualities of stone from all over England, as well as the effects of weathering and decay. His chapter on the testing of stone was well ahead of its time.

The first edition of Alec Clifton-Taylor's *The Pattern of English Building* was published in 1962. Clifton-Taylor's work includes both the geology and building qualities of the stone, but has somewhat more emphasis on the buildings than Howe's work, as would be expected from an Honorary Fellow of the Royal Institute of British Architects. He also contributed an introduction to the building stones of Dorset to Newman and Pevsner's volume in 'The Buildings of England' series, published in 1972. Within the text of Pevsner's book there is very little identification of the stone used in the buildings.

The main work specific to Dorset building stones was done by W.J. Arkell, a geologist. Following his detailed study of Jurassic geology published in 1933, he published a comparison of the names used for the beds of stone in the Purbeck and Portland stone quarries in the *Proceedings of the Dorset Natural History and Archaeological Society* in 1945 (vol. 66, 158-68).

There are many books written about the buildings in Dorset, listed in the Further Reading, but few include identification of stone. Most writers can recognise Portland stone, or Purbeck marble, but the local stone from parish quarries is usually referred to simply as 'rubble'. Each volume of the Royal Commission for Historical Monuments (1952 to 1975) concerning Dorset has an introduction on the geology of the district and the building stone available. However, the detailed descriptions of the buildings rarely include precise identifications of the stone. Articles on buildings in the *Dorset County Chronicle* usually refer to the place where the stone was obtained, such as 'Purbeck', or 'Ridgeway', which may geologically speaking be either of marine Portland or freshwater Purbeck limestone.

THE CURRENT STUDY

In the early 1980's a group of geologists recorded sites of geological interest under the National Scheme for Geological Site Documentation. These records are held in the Dorset Environmental Records Centre (DERC). At that time they examined the geology of many disused quarries. They noted the lithology (type of rock), the stratigraphy (its order in the geological timescale) and the palaeontology (fossils). Administrative details such as landownership and conservation status such as Site of Special Scientific Interest were also noted. One section of the documentation was left untouched – the history of the site.

While railway and road cuttings might be dated by reference to written records, discovering the history of the quarries has proved to be a more time-consuming exercise. The recording of the sites came to a premature end in 1987 when funding was withdrawn, after the whole of the Jurassic, but only

The tithe map for Bothenhampton drawn in 1845 shows three quarries in fields numbers 277, 289 and 298. © Dorset County Archives.

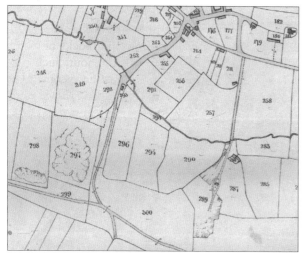

the Upper Greensand of the Cretaceous, had been documented.

In that year, with the support of the Geologists' Association Curry Fund, the author commenced research in the Dorset History Centre (County Record Office). Here tithe maps surveyed and drawn in the 1830's and 1840's provide the earliest published evidence of most quarries or pits by recording field names. Except in the parishes of Bothenhampton, Burstock and Langton Herring, no pictorial representation of quarries is given on the tithe maps. Their placing within a field is first shown on the Ordnance Survey maps of the 1880's and 1890's, at the scale of 6 inches to 1 mile, which were examined and compared with the tithe maps.

Further comparison with Ordnance Survey maps of the 1960's has produced an approximate grid reference for each quarry, which may be used to relate the old maps to the existing DERC records. On the late nineteenth century maps the legend quarry or old quarry indicated whether the site was in use at the time. On 1960's maps the description is disused. If a quarry is not shown on the late nineteenth century Ordnance Survey map, although the field name suggests its existence, it is presumed to have been out of use for a considerable time.

Research has shown that appropriate names were not always given to fields, for instance a huge quarry was dug in a field called Rickthorn in Bothenhampton. Medieval quarries, long disused, may have no clue on any map, and only fieldwork will find them. The huge quarry on the eastern side of Chapel Hill in Abbotsbury is a good example. In Langton Herring an earlier estate map (pre 1760) showing strip fields can be compared with the tithe map and the earliest Ordnance Survey map to identify quarries in use in the eighteenth century.

The original site recording was based on the study of articles in geological journals available in the Dorset County Museum. A wider search of journals in the library of Southampton University was undertaken for the compilation of a Bibliography and Index of Dorset Geology (Thomas & Ensom 1989). This has produced information on the stone available in specific quarries, which may act as examples of their immediate area. Comparison of stone of the same Formation in widely separated quarries illustrates the variability present in sedimentary rocks giving rise to the distinctive character of the stone used in separate villages.

There are few contemporary written records concerning quarrying, except for the large-scale industry of Portland and Purbeck. Some estate and parish records, held in the Dorset History Centre, have scattered references to quarrying, for instance at Horn Park, Broadwindsor (DRO/438A/T2-4, 22, from 1626 to 1896) and Waddon Hill, Stoke Abbott (DRO/D466/E5-7 during the years 1888 to 1899), where detailed ledgers survive of the building stone, roadstone and lime which were sold to customers in local villages, and on occasion to the City of London. Lime was charged at 1s 8d per hogshead, roadstone at 3s a load, and building stone at 4s a load.

Vouchers recording the use of stone in Stalbridge are in the accounts of the Anglesey Estate (DRO/D/ANG), describing the quarrying of Forest Marble limestone and sandstone for walling, paving, tile, trenching and highway stone. During the management of the estate from 1780 to 1854 both the Forest Marble and the Cornbrash limestone were quarried. In 1837 William Castleman, Steward to the Marquess of Anglesey, set out the prices of stone. 'Tile' – thin sandstones – at £1.10s.0d. a ton; 'paving' – sandstone or limestone – at 11s.0d. a ton; wall stone of best quality at Weston – Forest Marble limestone – at 2s.0d. a ton, from Harpits, best – Forest Marble – at 1s.0d. a ton. The different prices must reflect the different qualities of the stone from different quarries. In addition there are some nineteenth century building specifications and churchwardens accounts which refer to the source of stone by a parish or local name, though rarely a specific quarry.

Precise identification of the type of stone used in particular buildings has been minimal in previously published accounts. For the most part it is necessary to examine the buildings in each village. In order to judge the history of the local quarry, we need to know when each cottage, farmhouse or church was first built and the dates of any additions. A summary of historical detail can be found in the Historic Buildings Lists published by the Department of the Environment during the 1980's. These lists include considerably greater numbers of buildings than those listed in the Royal Commission volumes, are more detailed in their descriptions, and are more closely dated where this is possible. Styles of masonry can also provide a clue to the dates of construction and alterations and additions. In 1993 the author and Martin Hammond, an expert on brick manufacture, undertook a detailed study of the historic buildings in a selection of parishes across

Account books for Chartknolle and Waddon Hill from 1888-97 show the different costs of building stone, roadstone and hogsheads of lime for mortar [© Dorset County Archives D/SSA E5].

the county. This was funded by English Heritage, and recorded by John Lowe in 1994.

In 1993 a Dorset local group of the Geologists' Association was formed, and some of its members joined with the Dorset Environmental Records Centre, the Dorset County Museum and others to initiate the registration and conservation of Regionally Important Geological Sites. Many of the 60 sites registered to date (2007) were already documented, but others have been added as a result of the knowledge of individual geologists. These additions, and the recent re-surveying of much of the county by the British Geological Survey, have thrown further light on the use of stone as a building material.

Identifying the source of stone used in a particular building or village depends on knowledge of the local geology. In addition, use of an unfamiliar stone may require research into the history of a settlement. For instance, in Cerne Abbas the North Barn has its long walls of immense blocks of Chalk with flint randomly scattered throughout. Such huge blocks in a medieval building must have come from the local hill, where the remains of a very large old quarry can still be seen cut through the Lower and Middle Chalk. However, much of the Abbey buildings have stone reminiscent of the buildings in Upwey (limestone of Lower Purbeck age). A study of the history of the Abbey (Barker 1988) reveals that the Abbey estate included Poxwell, where a string of Lower Purbeck quarries runs round the southern side of the pericline. It is most probable, therefore, that the stone for the Abbey came from Poxwell.

DORSET BUILDING STONES

Listed by geological age, youngest first.

FORMATION	BUILDING STONE	ROCK TYPE	COLOUR.
Quaternary	*Weathered from Upper Chalk in the past 3 million years*		
Flint	Knapped flint	Silica nodules from Plateau gravel.	Black
		Silica nodules from Clay with Flints.	Black
Tertiary	*Palaeocene (65 to 56 million years old) and Eocene (56 to 35 million years old)*		
Barton Beds	Hengistbury ironstone	Ferruginous fine sandstone	Dark red
Poole Formation	Heathstone	Ferruginous sandstone, varying grain size, sub-rounded	Brown/orange
London Clay	Lytchett Matravers Sandstone	Ferruginous sandstone, even size grains, rounded	Dark brown/tan
Cretaceous	*145 to 65 million years old*		
Chalk	Flint	Silica nodules	Black or brown
	Chalk block (Clunch)	Coccolith limestone (Lower Chalk with glauconite grains) (Middle Chalk with flint nodules)	White
	Melbury Sandstone	Fine grained glauconitic calcareous sandstone.	Pale green
Upper Greensand	Eggardon Grit	Coarse glauconitic sandstone	Grey/green.
	Chert	Silica nodules	Blue, silver or tan
	Shaftesbury Sandstone	Glauconitic sandstone	Green
Wealden	Coarse Quartz Grit	Ferruginous sandstone	Red
Purbeck	Marble	*Viviparus* limestone	Blue, red or green
	Burr (Broken Shell Limestone)	Shell-fragment biosparite limestone	Cream
	Laning Vein	Sandy biosparite limestone	Cream

	Freestone Vein	Sandy biomicrite limestones (several beds with different fossil assemblages)	Cream or grey
	Downs Vein	Biomicrite limestone	Cream
	New Vein	Biomicrite limestone	Cream
	Cypris Freestones	Laminated micrite limestone	White
Jurassic	*205 to 145 million years old*		
Portland	'Portesham'	Pelletoid limestone	White
	on the Isle of Portland		
	Roach	Oolitic limestone with fossil cavities	White
	Whit Bed	Oolitic limestone with bivalve fossils	White
	Base Bed	Oolitic limestone	White
	on the Isle of Purbeck		
	Blue Bed	Oolitic limestone	White, weathering grey
	Spangle	Oolitic limestone with spar-filled fossils	White
	Pond Freestone	Oolitic limestone	White
	Under Freestone	Oolitic limestone	White
Corallian	*in north Dorset*		
	Todber Freestone	Oolitic limestone	Orange/cream
	Cucklington Oolite	Ferruginous oolitic limestone	Brown
	in south Dorset		
	Osmington Oolite	Oolitic limestone	Orange
Cornbrash	Cornbrash	Micritic limestone	Blue/grey
Forest Marble	(given local names)	Biosparite limestone	Grey
		Fine ripple-marked sandstone	Biscuit/light brown
Inferior Oolite	(given local names, Inc. Sherborne Building Stone)	Micrite limestone with some fossils	Cream/orange
Middle/Upper Lias	Junction Bed	Biosparite limestone	Pink, mottled, white
Middle Lias	Thorncombe Sand	Fine sandstone	Grey
Lower Lias	Blue Lias	Muddy limestone	Blue-grey.

CHAPTER TWO

Lower, Middle and Upper Lias

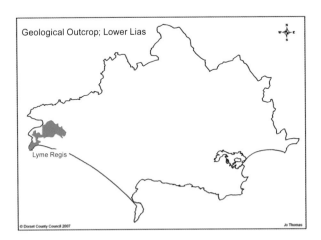

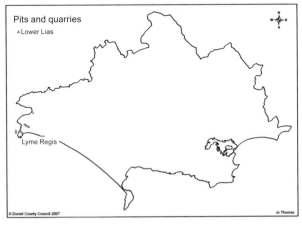

GEOLOGY

At the beginning of the Jurassic, about 205 million years ago, Dorset was under a shallow sea on the southern edge of a huge continent that included today's North America and Eurasia.

Lower Lias

The oldest of the Jurassic limestones, seen near Lyme Regis and Charmouth, is the Blue Lias. This series of limestones and shales was studied intensively by many of the early geologists because of the marine reptiles whose remains have been fossilised in fine organic-rich lime mud. Although the sea must have teemed with life, the sea floor mud was lacking in oxygen, so that any corpses that fell to the floor were not subject to rapid decomposition. Anaerobic decomposition created hydrogen sulphide and as the mud hardened into limestone or paper-thin shales, pyrite was formed from the sulphur and iron. The blue-grey colour of the limestone beds is due to finely disseminated pyrite. The alternation of limestone and shale may have been due to regular rhythmic changes in the marine environment leading to increases in carbonate (lime) deposition. Blue Lias limestone is a fine blue-grey micrite (powdery calcium carbonate).

Limestone and shale on the shore under Church Cliffs, Lyme Regis. Stone was quarried from the ledges and from the cliffs to the west of Lyme Regis.

The bed heights are variable, but typically around 15 centimetres. The limestone is very porous and tends to weather badly.

The names of the Blue Lias limestone beds given by quarrymen seem meaningless, but must originally have referred to the appearance of the limestone beds. They were recorded by W.D. Lang in 1924 – from top down: Table Ledge, Fish Bed, Grey Ledge,

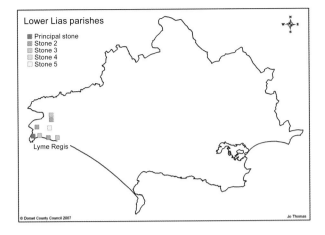

Glass Bottle, Top Quick, Venty, Best Bed, Second Bed, Rattle, Second Quick, Gumption, Third Quick, Top Tape, Top Copper, Mongrel, Second Mongrel, Specketty, Upper White, Upper Skulls, Iron Ledge, Under Copper, Under White, Lower Skulls, Lower Venty, Pigs Dirt, Brick Ledge. The intervening beds are shales. These beds were deposited over 4 million years in repeated cycles of limestone and shale that must reflect differing environmental conditions.

The beds that follow – the Shales with Beef, Black Ven Marls, Belemnite Marls and Green Ammonite Beds – lacked the carbonate needed to become limestone, but the last two have been used to make bricks in local kilns. The Shales with Beef have layers of calcite crystals that look like stringy beef when viewed sideways, the Belemnite Marls contain thousands of cigar shaped belemnite fossils, and the Green Ammonite Beds contain small ammonites filled with calcite crystals that often look green. Together they were deposited over 7 million years of geological time.

Middle Lias

The Middle Lias clays and fine sands were deposited nearer to the shoreline, with sea floor conditions varying in oxygen content. The Eype clay contains some fossils such as starfish, and the rare limestones include ammonites and belemnites. The Down Cliff Sands contain some pyrite nodules and are dark coloured, perhaps with an organic content. The Thorncombe Sands are orange, suggesting that the sea floor at that time was oxygenated, and any organic content has decomposed. In the Thorncombe Sands there are three lines of 'doggers', rounded boulders of sandstone that have formed during lithification by concentration of calcium carbonate within the sandy sediment. The inside of these doggers is grey, where the iron content has not oxidised, showing that the porosity of the doggers is lower than the unconsolidated sand. These differing clays and sands were deposited over 5 million years.

The Marlstone Rock Bed and the Junction Bed limestone, spanning the Middle and Upper Lias, were deposited in shallow water. The lower half, of iron-rich oolite, was followed by lime mud containing the remains of ammonites, belemnites and bivalves. This hardened rapidly in warm, tropical water, but was partly eroded away by wave action. The resulting limestone now appears mottled in colour because of the mix of sediments and contains 7 different ammonite zones which were deposited over about 8 million years. This is known as a condensed deposit. It is a sparite limestone, in most places not much more than a metre thick, but on the cliff at Fault Corner near Eype Mouth it is much thicker. It is thought that the fault must have been moving, leaving a deep trough to be filled with sediment.

Upper Lias

About 180 million years ago, the Upper Lias above the Junction Bed was the Down Cliff Clay formed in deeper water and Bridport Sands as the sea shallowed again. Deposited in about 4 million years, the two together now measure nearly 70 metres thick. The sand formed as a huge sandbank that moved south eastwards across the sea floor that is now Somerset

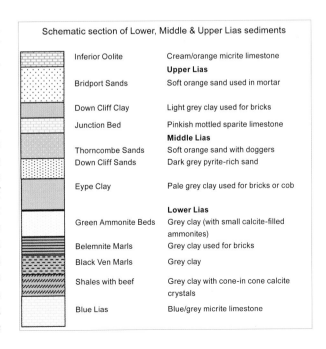

and Dorset. Repeated hard bands in the Bridport Sand contain a greater proportion of calcium carbonate (lime) and gradually appear closer together until at the top of the sequence about 6 metres of limestone beds have formed.

This is the Inferior Oolite, in which one bed is packed with fossils of ammonites, belemnites and bivalves, indicating very slow deposition of lime mud to cover the corpses. The beds above have fewer fossils, as deposition increased, but the ammonites vary from place to place in Dorset. This suggests that deposits of different ages have been preserved, possibly in shallow depressions on the contemporary sea floor, or as a result of fault movements at the time.

The limestone used as building stone has few fossils, and is an orange/cream micrite, with occasional ooliths (round balls of calcite). As the lime mud would have formed in comparatively quiet sea conditions, and ooliths usually form in wave-scoured water, it is thought that the ooliths were swept into the quiet waters by occasional storms. The thickness of the beds of Inferior Oolite is variable, and it is sometimes thick enough to be cut as ashlar. These limestones cover 7 million years of geological time.

LANDSCAPE
The Marshwood Vale
The hills on the coast and around the Marshwood Vale are topped by the Upper Greensand, a much younger sandstone (112 million years ago). This was deposited on a Jurassic land surface that had been planed-off by millions of years of weathering, after sea level rose again in the Cretaceous. The Blue Lias limestone and Lower Lias clays form the lower slopes of these hills on the western side of the Vale. All the Lower Lias can be seen in the cliffs from Lyme Regis to Golden Cap.

Because all the Jurassic rocks are dipping slightly to the east in Dorset, the Middle Lias clays and fine sands form the lower slopes of the eastern side of the Vale, below the Chalk ridge near Rampisham. On the coast the Middle Lias begins under Golden Cap and continues to Fault Corner east of Eype Mouth.

The full succession of beds into the Upper Lias on the coast is interrupted by two faults at Fault Corner and in the western cliff at West Bay, but continues on the eastern cliff towards Burton Bradstock. The Bridport Sands form spectacular cliffs between West

Bay and Burton Bradstock, with the Inferior Oolite at the top nearer to Burton Bradstock.

There are many small faults around Bridport and Beaminster, resulting in a confused jumble of small hills, like Sloes Hill and Colmer's Hill in Symondsbury or Hyde Hill in Walditch. A few of these hills are topped by the Junction Bed, like the ridge north of Bradpole, but most by the Inferior Oolite limestones, with the softer sand underneath easily weathered by water to give steep sided hills. In the areas from Chideock to Powerstock and Burton Bradstock in the south, and from Drimpton to Mapperton in the north, each parish had at least one quarry in the limestone that topped all the hills. The detailed character of the limestone varies slightly from place to place, due to varying sea floor conditions and fault movements at the time of deposition.

The Yeo Valley between Sherborne and Yeovil
Near Yeovil the Bridport Sands are known as the Yeovil Sands, but are clearly the same Formation, and can be seen in deep cuttings rather than on the cliffs. North of the main road between Yeovil and Sherborne the eastward dip of the beds brings the Junction Bed to the surface around Trent, but by Nether Compton the Inferior Oolite forms the summit of the hills. On the hill slope on the northern side of Sherborne, from Sandford Lane to Milborne Port, the beds of the Inferior Oolite are considerably thicker than elsewhere and it is thought that the Poyntington Fault to the east of the town was moving at the time, creating a trough that was filled with a greater depth of lime mud. This fault, with the eastern side uplifted, has created a prominent hill.

USE OF BUILDING STONES
Lower Lias – Blue Lias
The Blue Lias limestones are used for building in Lyme Regis but tend to weather badly and have often been covered with render, or hung with slates. The eighteenth century Dorset historian, John Hutchins, recorded 200 houses in 1774, of blue rag-stone, 'not very durable and covered with blue slate'. The Blue Lias can be seen in the walls by the river, the Town Mill, Drake's Way and the Borough Offices, but many buildings have been rendered and painted. The fourteenth century Buddle Bridge, and the walls of the river leading to it, are still in good condition,

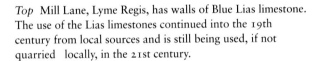

Top Mill Lane, Lyme Regis, has walls of Blue Lias limestone. The use of the Lias limestones continued into the 19th century from local sources and is still being used, if not quarried locally, in the 21st century.

Above A slate-hung wall in Lyme Regis. Hutchins, the Dorset historian, recorded in 1774 that there were 200 houses 'of blue rag-stone, not very durable, and covered with blue slate'.

Above right Lyme Regis Town Mill was run by water power from the stream, and was built of Blue Lias limestone.

succeeding generations of engineers having taken good care of it. In the eighteenth century the limestones were used for stucco or interior plasterwork. From 1800 to 1920 the limestone was used to make lime for mortar, being quarried from the cliffs and from the offshore reefs. The latter method has proved a mistake, as the reefs no longer protect the town from the sea.

Charmouth Cement Mill was built in 1850's next to the beach, and was only working for seventeen years. The limestone was brought by horse and cart or in baskets by women, two to a basket. As there are no ledges of Blue Lias at Charmouth, they collected loose stones from the beach for the raw material, but this material was soon exhausted, which would account for the short life of the mill. The limestone was burnt and then crushed by two grinding stones of imported 'granite' (the millstone remaining is typically French), which were run by a steam engine. There were two lime kilns at the back of the mill. The women also carried away the cement, which weighed 40 lbs a basket, and were paid 3 pence per basket. The mill was included in a land sale in 1867, but was probably not worked again. This was about the time that the manufacture of Portland cement started. Royalties of ls 6d a ton of cement were mentioned in the sale.

On the western edge of the Marshwood Vale some of the farmhouses, and many boundary walls, are built of a blue limestone. Local residents believe it has come from pits in the Vale where the Belemnite Marls that were used for brickmaking include one bed of limestone – the Belemnite Stone. In Wootton Fitzpaine the most common building material is chert, but Knapp Farm (1700) also has Blue Lias and Inferior Oolite.

Much of the Blue Lias used for paving in Dorset has come from inland quarries in Uplyme in Devon and Keinton Mandeville in Somerset. It is a blue-grey fine-grained stone with no bedding visible. It has also been used for kerbstones, and can still be seen in Sherborne and Shaftesbury, though it is being replaced by a dark igneous rock which is harder wearing. When used for paving it is sometimes possible to see oysters on the surface of Blue Lias.

Middle Lias

Middle Lias sandy beds were too soft for building except for the doggers of the Thorncombe Sands that have been used for foundation stones for the brick outer shell of Bettiscombe Manor. When Bettiscombe Manor was being renovated it was possible to see the medieval cruck construction of the inner walls, where the timber frame was infilled with Inferior Oolite limestone from Grange quarry in Burstock. Outside the house, trenches were being dug for drains and the foundations of the brick eighteenth century house were uncovered. The fine grey sandstone blocks were unexpected, but were soon identified with the doggers in the Thorncombe Sands on Sliding Hill, above the manor house. The house had been in the Pinney family for centuries, but was sold prior to its renovation in the early 1990's.

Manor Farm stable block in Symondsbury also includes a few blocks from the Thorncombe Sands doggers in the rubble walls. The doggers can be seen in Mill Lane, to the east of the stables.

In the past Eype Clay was used to make cob in Symondsbury parish, though most of the buildings have now disintegrated. The pits from which the clay was dug are known as marlpits, a term which occurs on many tithe maps and therefore will provide clues to the use of clay for cob construction. Eype Clay was also dug from marlpits in Trent, and probably also used for cob. Cob buildings in other parishes throughout Dorset would have used their own local clay.

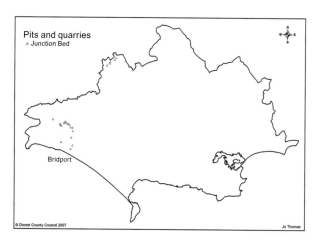

Upper Lias – Junction Bed

On the eastern edge of the Marshwood Vale the Middle Lias clays and silts, topped by the Junction Bed, are overlain by the Upper Lias Bridport Sands and the Inferior Oolite limestone which is the most important building stone from Broadwindsor southwards. However, where streams have cut deep valleys through the Bridport Sands there are occasional small outcrops of Junction Bed limestone. Although rarely used for building, it has provided firm foundations at Symondsbury and Melplash.

Symondsbury is built on an outcrop of the Junction Bed underlying the village, which was quarried north of Manor Farm. It is only used in barn walls, as the Inferior Oolite available from the hills above proved to be a better stone. Here the colour of the Junction Bed limestone is mottled pink and white. Bradpole also has some Junction Bed limestone in rough walls.

In 1828-9 an agreement to build a house in

St Gabriel's Farmhouse is built of blue limestone and bricks make from the Middle Lias Eype Clay in the fields nearby.

Junction Bed limestone in Symondsbury Manor Farm stable block. The darker lines are fossil shells. This wall has blocks of all the different stones available in the village, Inferior Oolite (a lighter orange), Forest Marble (dark grey with shells), and a few smooth grey blocks of Thorncombe Sands doggers from Mill Lane.

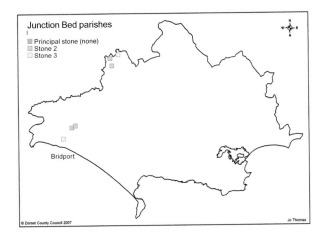

The Chantry, Trent, a fourteenth century building using Junction Bed limestone from the village.

Netherbury, by Joseph & Frederick Galpin, builders, specifies that the cellar walls should be of stone from Bowood quarry. There were five different quarries in the Junction Bed in North Bowood. The stone for the upper walls was not specified, but could have been Junction Bed or Inferior Oolite, which was also available in the parish. The paving in the kitchen and cellar was of Purbeck pavement, and Portland stone was used for columns, steps, cills and hearth stones. The stable was to be built of unspecified stone and 'pitched with Banton stone' (Forest Marble from Bothenhampton). The house roof was to be of Cornish slate, and 'the front of the house to be composed with blue lias mortar and jointed'. The quarries in North Bowood provided some stone for building, but most of the houses in Netherbury appear to be of Inferior Oolite. Perhaps most Junction Bed was used for lime burning as it tends to be rubbly.

Outcrops of Junction Bed north of the Sherborne to Yeovil road are cut into small blocks by faults and in

The Junction Bed limestone, quarried for the church from a field in Trent still known as Churchfields, is almost white. The prominent lines are fossil shells.

part of the central area of Nether Compton it made good foundations. It has been quarried at Trent and Sandford Orcas. Here the stone is white and some pieces contain many small ammonites. In the church at Trent the thirteenth century nave and north chapel are built of the white Junction Bed, as is the early fourteenth century south tower. Local knowledge suggests that the stone came from a field known as Church Hills, or Churchill, but the quarry has been ploughed in. The spire (rebuilt 1908-9) and porch are Junction Bed with Ham Hill Stone buttresses. The fifteenth century Chantry near the church is built of the Junction Bed, with the later chimney possibly White Lias from Camel Hill in Somerset. There were two other Junction Bed quarries in the parish. There are three manor houses and large farms in Trent, some built of Inferior Oolite from parishes to the south, but many of the barns and smaller houses include Junction Bed.

Garden walls at Sandford Orcas Manor have pieces of Junction Bed limestone, quarried from Shillers Lane. Trent and Sandford Orcas were previously in Somerset and much of their building stone comes from there. A fine white laminated stone used in Sandford Orcas manor (mid sixteenth century) and Church Farm (fifteenth and seventeenth centuries) its barn (eighteenth century), and several cottages in Trent, is not a native of Dorset. It comes from Camel Hill, Somerset, several miles to the north. In Hummer, Anchor Farm (1617) and its barns are of White Lias. Lyes House (seventeenth century) has a brick front, but the north wall has been built of Blue Lias up to 5 feet high, then White Lias above. With Inferior Oolite on its eastern wall, this is a delight to the eye!

CHAPTER THREE

Inferior Oolite

Geologically the Inferior Oolite is a logical continuation of the Upper Lias, but as a building stone it is so important and widely used in West Dorset that it deserves its own chapter.

There are two separate areas of West Dorset where the Inferior Oolite is quarried. Between Burton Bradstock and Drimpton near Broadwindsor there were 138 quarries in a total of 20 parishes. Many of the quarries are isolated on the top of the small hills such as Jacks Hill and Mythe Hill near Mapperton, or Chideock Quarry Hill. Near Loders, Bell quarry is cut into the side of a steep hill where the Bridport Sands has been moved higher than the Inferior Oolite on the north side of a fault. Near Sherborne the outcrop of the Inferior Oolite, with 48 quarries, is continuous from Nether Compton to Oborne.

BROADWINDSOR TO THE COAST

Only Chideock quarry and Grange quarry in Burstock are shown on the first edition of the 1 inch Ordnance Survey map surveyed in 1794, with the latter mentioned in a lease of 1691. The complex of buildings at Childhay Manor is mostly of Inferior Oolite, almost certainly from Grange quarry, including a sixteenth century barn.

Apart from field names on tithe maps the only written records of quarrying are evidence from nineteenth century Ordnance Survey maps and an account book from Waddon Hill and Chartknolle Stoke Abbott. The lime ledgers of Henry Smith for 1888-99 include sales of building stone, hogsheads of lime, roadstone and rubble to customers as widely spread as Thorncombe and Burton Bradstock. Lime was charged at 1s 8d per hogshead; roadstone at 3s a load; building stone at 4s a load, with hauling added to the cost of the load. At one time there were five limekilns on the hill using the waste stone and the

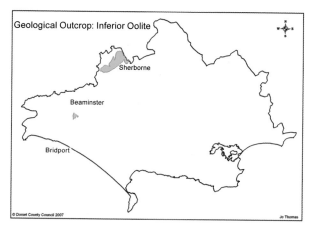

Many of the areas underlain by Inferior Oolite are covered by the succeeding Fuller's Earth Clay, or are too small to map at this scale.

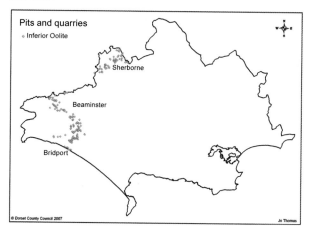

rubbly beds above the building stone. The quarries on Waddon Hill may have been the earliest used, as the Romans built a camp there.

The succession common to all the quarries is thin sandy limestones at the bottom, under a thicker bed of sparite full of fossils, followed above by varying numbers of beds up to 1 metre thick. In many quarries near Beaminster is a red-stained bed, but the building stone beds are a fine powdery

Crepe Farm barn in Symondsbury has been built of the Wild Bed and the Scissum Bed of the Inferior Oolite. These beds are not the best building stone, but were used for outbuildings on the farm. The blocks often contain fossils and contain a good proportion of iron, causing the deep orange colour.

Above Crepe Farm in Symondsbury, probably built with Inferior Oolite limestone from Sloes' Hill or Watton Hill in Bridport.

Below Brook House at Yondover was built of Inferior Oolite from the Loders quarries.

micrite, cream to orange in colour, with few fossils. Above these building stone beds rubbly beds occur in many quarries. The quarries are usually less than 4 metres deep. Many quarries could provide stone of sufficient thickness and quality to be cut as ashlar, so that the manor house, church and vicarage of a village would be built of the best stone in ashlar, while the cottages were of dressed stone, and the farm buildings were rubble.

The abundance and type of fossils is often characteristic of a particular bed or quarry. In Symondsbury village the old rectory west of the church is of Inferior Oolite ashlar, whereas Rectory Cottage is of dressed stone. The stable block on Mill Lane has a mixture of every stone available. Crepe Farm and its barn, set apart from the village, have been built of a much darker orange Inferior Oolite, identified in Sloes Hill and Watton Hill quarries as the Wild Bed. The barn, now part of the industrial estate, has blocks of stone containing belemnites and bivalves and even the algal 'snuff-boxes' from the Yellow Conglomerate near the base of the limestones.

At Stoke Abbott the rubble used in some barn walls is rich in belemnites, whereas at Burton Bradstock the cottage walls below the church contain many brachiopods. In this southern area in the quarries such as Stony Head Loders, Chideock Hill, Waddon Hill, Stoke Abbott and Horn Park, Broadwindsor, the Burton Limestone, referred to by quarrymen as the Top Limestone, is in the Parkinsoni Zone, named after the principal ammonite.

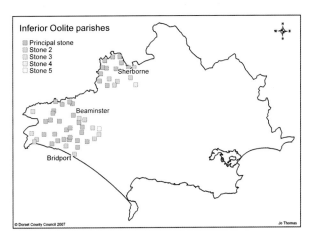

Inferior Oolite parishes

■ Principal stone
■ Stone 2
■ Stone 3
■ Stone 4
□ Stone 5

Sherborne

Beaminster

Bridport

© Dorset County Council 2007   Jo Thomas

Above Bell Quarry limekiln is north of Loders near a cottage that used to be an inn. It was closed down when the railway navvies caused too much trouble!

Below Whetley Cross Quarry, north of Broadwindsor, produced a fine cream micrite (powdery) limestone from the Inferior Oolite.

The earlier history of the quarries must be found in the buildings. Many of those listed as historic or of architectural merit are recorded as seventeenth century, though on examination they would appear to have been originally built earlier. A few, such as Bettiscombe Manor have medieval construction somewhere inside a later building. Many churches can be traced back to the Norman rebuilding of Saxon places of worship. Powerstock church has a Norman chancel arch with dog-tooth carving, supported by six columns each carved with a different ornament. At Loders the church walls are of the local Inferior Oolite, but stand on a plinth of Forest Marble limestone from Bothenhampton. The east wall of Loders church was repaired during the nineteenth century from Chiselcombe quarry on the northern side of the road at Loders Cross.

All the village buildings are of stone originally from their own parish quarries, but these may have been worked out by the nineteenth century when the best quality stone was said to come from Whetley Cross, Horn Park and Barrowfield in Beaminster. The quarry on Allington Hill, Bridport, was worked out during the eighteenth century but had been used for the thirteenth century hospital of St. Mary Magdalen.

The town of Beaminster was surrounded by quarries in the Inferior Oolite that have provided stone for all the buildings until well into the twentieth century. Local people can remember that quarrying was carried on when the weather was unsuitable for farm work, rather than being a trade in itself. Mr. Perry of Hogshill Street remembered that the best bed was known as the White Bed, and that when they tried drilling holes for dynamite the heat and moisture turned the powdered rock to cement. The stone could only be won by pick or mechanical shovel. A grab with a single tine was used after the First World War and the men were paid by the cubic yard and the size of the rocks, so they learnt to make it look good.

At the sale of Barrowfield Farm in 1920, which included a quarry, records show that the 'Right of taking stone was let to Mr. G. Symes on payment of a Royalty of 1s 6d per yard for Building Stone and 9d per yard for stone taken for Road making'.

Around Mapperton there were several small quarries and records remain of the building of the Rectory from a quarry in its own garden in 1699 to 1703. Ham Hill Stone was bought for the door and window surrounds, pavement was purchased from Axminster. The building lime was made from local stone, but plastering lime came from Uplyme. The manor house at Mapperton has an entrance façade of Ham Hill Stone, but the rear facing the garden is of Inferior Oolite, possibly dug on site. Charity Ground Quarry is said to be the site of the burial of the villagers of Mapperton who were wiped out by the Black Death. There was a tree at the entrance to the lane known as the 'Posy Tree', referring to the nursery rhyme 'Ring-a-ring-a-roses' which is said to come from the ring of spots caused by the Black Death. The tree didn't look too healthy last time I saw it.

Powerstock is a good example of a village that has continued to use Inferior Oolite from its own

Left & above The Inferior Oolite used in the Norman chancel arch and pillars of Powerstock church is a pale colour, but mottled orange with iron staining. The Inferior Oolite changes so rapidly from one quarry to another that each village, using its own quarry, has a distinctive character.

quarries over many centuries. A motte and bailey castle was built in 1205 to the east of the present village. Hutchins' *History of Dorset* in 1770 refers to vaults and standing walls of stone, but it has all disappeared, probably used for later houses in the village. The church has a twelfth century chancel arch and the core of the tower. In the fourteenth century the north and south arcades were added, and in the fifteenth the tower and buttress and the south doorway. In 1845-9 the chancel was rebuilt, lined with ashlar of 'native stone'. The entire building is of Inferior Oolite. The houses now standing in the village date from the sixteenth to the nineteenth centuries, though Mappercombe Manor has a fifteenth century portion. West Milton church was originally built in the twelfth and thirteenth centuries, suggesting that there were previously more dwellings close by, but it was demolished and its stone re-used for a primary school in Powerstock in 1848.

A good many churches were rebuilt during the nineteenth century, when new houses were built, or old ones renovated. St. Andrews chapel in Bradpole is recorded by Hutchins (1863) as having been recently built of Inferior Oolite from Loders, with dressings of Ham Hill stone. St. Mary's church in

Bridport (1362 and 1486) is almost entirely Inferior Oolite, including the rebuilt chancel and aisles of 1860. This stone could have come from Allington Hill or Hyde Hill quarries. The Hyde hill quarries provided Inferior Oolite for the nineteenth century buildings in Walditch, including the mansion house, the real tennis court and the church. The garden wall at Hyde House is built of stone which is particularly rich in brachiopods. In the nineteenth century

In the walls of Walditch church the Inferior Oolite contains many fossil shells. The quarry from which this came is on Hyde Hill, where the bats have made their home in the underground workings.

Ham Hill Stone is strong enough to retain a carving, such as this ship on the tower of Whitchurch Canonicorum church.

Low's Hill Quarry, on the western side of Sherborne, is about 3m deep and one of more than a dozen quarries in the Inferior Oolite in the area. Their stone is darker and more thinly bedded than the stone from north of Sherborne in the Sherborne Building Stone, although it is the same age. This quarry is now a Site of Special Scientific Interest.

cottages were built in Loders for workers in the net and rope industry of Inferior Oolite with brick window surrounds. The building of the railways in the nineteenth century meant that it was possible to bring Bath stone into Dorset, where it was used in the dressings of Catherston Leweston church.

All the villages that had Inferior Oolite limestone quarries used it, with those near to Bridport incorporating the Forest Marble limestone from Bothenhampton as a damp-proof foundation. Many of the villages within the Vale of Marshwood used the Inferior Oolite, as the Lower Lias blue limestones were not of such good quality. However, on the western edge of the Vale, from Stanton St. Gabriel northwards, the Chert from the Upper Greensand was the most prominent building material. Lamberts Castle, Coneys Castle, Pilsdon Pen, Hardown Hill and Langdon Hill all had gravel pits providing chert nodules.

The church of St. Candida in Whitchurch Canonicorum, founded in 1170, is a good example of the use of every stone available at different times. The parish of Whitchurch Canonicorum is dominated by Hardown Hill, which has provided the majority of the building materials – the chert from the Upper Greensand. Both chert and grit from the Upper Greensand were used originally but by the thirteenth century Inferior Oolite from Chideock quarry hill had become the main material. The interior is entirely Inferior Oolite, including the delicate carving on the capitals. The Norman south wall (1170) includes chert and Upper Greensand grit rubble, and a few Roman tiles. The eastern end (1200) has Forest Marble and chert, the nearest source of the former being Bothenhampton. The north transept, dated thirteenth to fourteenth centuries, has chert, Inferior Oolite a blue Lower Lias limestone and more Roman tiles. The west tower (1400) is of Inferior Oolite with Ham Hill Stone dressings; high on the eastern side is a carving of a ship. Different methods of dressing and building with chert can be compared in the fifteenth century south porch and the 1822 south vestry of the church. St. Wite's tomb in the north chapel has a Purbeck Marble slab on top, with a huge slab below that has been painted, but might be Purbeck Burr limestone. The 1847-8 east wall of the chancel includes chert, blue limestone, Inferior Oolite and Upper Greensand grit. The gargoyles are made of Ham Hill Stone.

THE YEO VALLEY AND SHERBORNE

In the Yeo valley, the Inferior Oolite that was quarried west of Sherborne, around Bradford Abbas and Nether Compton, is darker in colour than the south Dorset stone, with more fossils.

In contrast the Sherborne Building Stone has less iron and is therefore paler in colour than most of the other parishes. Quarried from a much thicker deposit on the northern side of Sherborne itself, it has provided stone for the town, the Abbey and its associated buildings, the two castles and the nineteenth century school buildings. A good proportion of this stone has been cut as ashlar. There are several hundred listed buildings dating from the twelfth to the nineteenth centuries. Two quarries can still be seen on the western side of the Bristol Road, in Quarr Lane. The first is in the public open space, the second further north, but behind a locked gate to prevent fly-tipping.

In Sandford Orcas at Jerrards the sixteenth century barn is of random rubble, some blocks being brown with broken shell material, some cream with recognisable belemnites and bivalves and several concentric circles which were algal in origin. Joints filled with calcite crystals can also be seen. These blocks may have come from the Compton quarries. On the yard side there are larger blocks of Sherborne Building Stone, which is also used for the quoins. The window mullions in the barn are fashioned from Ham Hill Stone and the huge roof is thatched. The earliest part of the main house facing south is of random rubble, but the east facing façade (sixteenth century) is of dressed, coursed stone. The porch, of

Above Much of Sherborne is built of the Sherborne Building Stone (Inferior Oolite) from local quarries. The earliest quarries were near the present day hospital and as time went on the quarrying moved northward up Blackberry Lane, Sandford Lane and near Oborne.

Below The 15th century St John's Almshouses in Sherborne were built from a quarry near the Newell stream. The windows are framed in Ham Hill Stone. The roof is covered with Forest Marble sandstone tiles from quarries in Sherborne deer park.

Above Jerrards, a group of buildings just outside Sandford Orcas, is built of Inferior Oolite from the Sandford Lane quarries north of Sherborne. The porch of the main house is of Doulting Stone, another Inferior Oolite limestone from Somerset that contains many shining crinoid plates.

Right A cottage next to St John's Almshouses is built of Inferior Oolite rubble stone.

Above A sample of Ham Hill Stone in a Sherborne building.

Below The Ham Hill Stone figures on the west tower of St Mary's church , Beaminster. At the bottom is the Crucifixion, with the Resurrection and the Ascension of Christ above.

a pale creamy ashlar, could be of Sherborne Building Stone, until the use of a magnifying glass shows the occasional piece of crinoid stem and a gritty texture which is more likely to be from the Doulting quarries – also Inferior Oolite, but from Somerset. To the right of the seventeenth century porch the courses of Inferior Oolite look more even and diminish in size towards the eaves. At the far end of the house the stone in a twentieth century addition is regimented by comparison. On the garden front, facing west

a seventeenth century bay is entirely in Ham Hill Stone. The Dairy House on the eastern side of the yard was rebuilt during 1993 using the original Inferior Oolite Sherborne Building Stone. The north façade of the eighteenth century stables is original, but new stone was required for the 1993 renovation at the side and back. These three buildings have stone tiled roofs. The yard is paved with large Blue Lias paving slabs.

In Sherborne and some of the villages, roof tiles are of thin shelly limestones or ripple-marked sandstones from the Forest Marble quarries on Lillington Hill and Longburton to the south of the town.

HAM HILL STONE

Ham Hill Stone is of similar age to the Inferior Oolite and is thought to have formed as a bank of shells filling a valley cut through the Bridport (Yeovil) Sands by flowing water. It has been quarried since the middle ages at Ham Hill, Montacute near Yeovil. The hill now stands proud of the surrounding plain as the sands have been weathered away. The deposit of iron-cemented broken shell material is about 50 ft thick and strongly current-bedded.

Throughout these two areas of West Dorset several prestigious manor houses and churches have used Ham Hill Stone. This iron-rich shelly limestone consists of tiny pieces of shell, all lying flat and packed tightly together. It can be carved when fresh from the quarry and hardens to provide hard-wearing ashlar. It retains its strength when used vertically, and is therefore used for door cases and window mullions, particularly in Inferior Oolite buildings. In some cases, such as Parnham, only the façade is Ham Hill Stone, the rear is Inferior Oolite.

The church in Beaminster is mostly Inferior Oolite, with a Ham Hill Stone tower built about 1500. It has 41 pinnacles of a Gothic design. The plinth of each pinnacle rests on a carving of a devil or mythical animal. Two statues on the corner are St. Bega, a Saxon saint whose name was given to the town – 'Begamynster' – and King Alfred. On the west face of the tower are a Madonna and Child, flanked by saints; a Crucifixion flanked by St. John and St. Mary; and the Resurrection and Ascension flanked by a pilgrim with staff and scallop shell hat badge, and a figure holding a fuller's bat and mill. The last figure represents Beaminster's flax trade.

CHAPTER FOUR

Forest Marble and Cornbrash

GEOLOGY

About 160 million years ago, following about ten million years in which the Fuller's Earth Clay was deposited in fairly deep water, the Dorset part of the continental shelf became shallower due to continental movement. It was still in a sub-tropical environment, so that the temperature remained warm enough to encourage the formation of limestones. The depth of the sea varied over the next three or four million years and this is reflected in the succession of clays, sands and limestones in the Forest Marble and Cornbrash Formations.

In Dorset the majority of the Forest Marble Formation consists of clays; the lower clay unit containing subsidiary sand and silt and an upper unit of clay with more sandstone beds of varying thickness. About half way through the sequence are beds of shelly limestone, some thin, some massive.

The clays of the Forest Marble Formation formed in comparatively deep water, commencing about 165 million years ago, but the shelly limestones are thought to be the result of shallow water shoals brought together by storms. The rich but mostly broken fossil content includes brachiopods, bivalves and gastropods, with the only whole fossils lying on the top surface of the individual beds. During lithification (process of hardening into rock over millions of years) the broken shells have partly dissolved and recrystallised to form a crystalline calcite cement between the broken shell material. The stone is particularly strong and impervious because the crystalline calcite cement leaves few pore spaces for the water to penetrate. Because the limestone formed as isolated shoals, they are laterally discontinuous and the beds vary in thickness. The quarries are therefore scattered across the outcrop of the Formation without any apparent pattern. Interleaved within some of the patches of limestone are further sandstone beds.

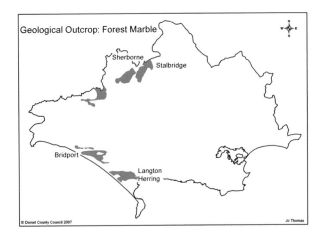

Geological Outcrop: Forest Marble

Sherborne

Stalbridge

Bridport

Langton Herring

© Dorset County Council 2007

Jo Thomas

The hard, crystalline, fossiliferous, sparite limestone provides the best quality building stone, particularly in the Bothenhampton quarries where it can be thick enough to cut as ashlar. It is often replaced laterally with less well-cemented limestones with a considerable clay content. The sandstone is found as separate patches, as well as interleaved with the shelly limestone. A patch can be seen on

Forest Marble shelly limestone consists of broken shells cemented together by crystalline calcite [as seen through a handlens].

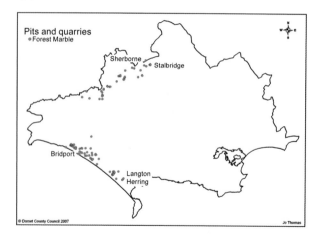

Pits and quarries
• Forest Marble
Sherborne • Stalbridge
Bridport
Langton Herring
© Dorset County Council 2007   Jo Thomas

West Hill, Sherborne (on the Dorchester road south from the town), where an outcrop of the sandstone is up to a metre thick and there are several thinner sandstone beds further down the hill. There were several quarries at this level on the hill, both east in Sherborne Park and west towards Lillington.

The Cornbrash limestones formed in shallow water and represent two phases of rising sea levels. There is a distinct change of fauna between each and therefore a considerable gap in time. The Lower Cornbrash, which gradually oversteps (as if sea levels are rising 'across country') the Forest Marble, occasionally has a pebble bed at the base, indicating a beach. The lowest bed of limestone is a hard massive blue-hearted limestone, with rubbly cream coloured limestones and marls above. The base of the Upper Cornbrash is seen as a normal bedding plane, the sequence starting with a sandy marl followed by a limestone with a hummocky top where it has been eroded.

LANDSCAPE

The Forest Marble Formation is found at outcrop in two areas of Dorset separated by the Cretaceous Chalk downland. In the north-west there is a north east to south west belt between Stalbridge and Halstock, and in the south-west it occurs from Watton Cliff near Bridport to Radipole north of Weymouth.

Many of the quarries for Forest Marble building stone in the northern area are cut through the Cornbrash limestone lying above on the surface. In this case the clays above the Forest Marble limestones are thin enough to present no problem of

excessive overburden. Although both limestones will be more resistant to weathering than the clays, the hills are not particularly prominent except for West Hill, Sherborne, where the River Yeo has cut deeply through the Fullers' Earth Clays beneath the Forest Marble.

In the southern area Watton Cliff is composed of the lower clay, with a capping of the Forest Marble shelly limestone. At Fault Corner it is possible to climb up the slumped clay and collect small thin pieces of the fine sandstone 'tiles' with trace fossils on both upper and lower surfaces. The outcrop is broken by two faults and re-appears on Wych Hill south of Bothenhampton. This is a prominent ridge that runs eastward through Swyre and Bexington, disappearing under the Chalk downland north of Abbotsbury. Faults bring it to the surface again in the hill south of Langton Herring where it appears in the core of the Weymouth Anticline.

Near the south coast the Cornbrash limestone forms the hill running from Shipmoor Point at Abbotsbury Swannery along Chesters Hill, Rodden Ridge to the north of Langton Herring and through Buckland Ripers to Nottington. This outcrop is on the northern limb of the Weymouth Anticline, whereas on the southern limb the outcrop runs through East Fleet and Chickerell.

QUARRYING AND USE IN BUILDINGS

The Forest Marble shelly limestone is used for all the buildings close to the quarries. In addition, in localities where the main building stone available is a micrite with a powdery texture, such as Inferior Oolite, Forest Marble limestone is used for the plinths and foundation courses of walls. Forest Marble absorbs little water and has an exceptional load bearing quality. It can therefore be used for damp courses, bridges, water mills and as strengthening for river banks, often requiring it to be carried some distance from the quarries. The fine sandstone that is found either separately or interleaved with the limestone is equally water resistant and has been used for roof tiles, foundations and for bridges.

Southern Area

The large quarries on Wych Hill, Bothenhampton provided stone for Bridport and its surrounding area. Quarrying here dates back to the fourteenth century, and there have been as many as twelve quarries over the centuries, two of which were still working into the 1940's.

The stone houses in Bridport and Allington are built with either Forest Marble or Inferior Oolite, though many of the eighteenth and nineteenth century houses are of brick. The Forest Marble is said not to 'sweat' in cold weather, and is tougher than the Inferior Oolite, so it has been preferred for use in industrial buildings.

Ropemaking has been the main industry in Bridport since the thirteenth century and until the invention of machines in the early nineteenth century the rope was made in rope walks in the alleyways of the town. The finer twine was made by the women in or immediately outside their cottages in the surrounding parishes. After the invention of machines in 1812 several rope factories were built of Forest Marble. The factory in West Street was built in the late eighteenth century for the Gundry family. Rope was made from hemp and twine for nets from flax, both grown locally. It is my impression that the hemp was grown on sandy soil and the flax on clay soil. Rope and twine are today spun with man-made fibres.

The fourteenth century Chantry and the sixteenth century Museum building in South Street are both built of Forest Marble, with Ham Hill Stone dressings. However, St. Mary's church, originally built in the thirteenth century is almost entirely of Inferior Oolite. With both limestones available on either side of Bridport it may simply have been a matter of choice.

Several nineteenth century building specifications in the Dorset History Centre specify Baunton (the local pronunciation of Bothenhampton) stone for

Factory buildings in Bridport, part of the rope industry, were built of Forest Marble shelly limestone from Bothenhampton. This provided a strong building to house machinery, and a dry environment in which to work. It is said that the stone from Bothenhampton did not 'sweat' in the winter.

cellars and flooring as well as bridges and walls by the river, particularly the Pymore Mills factory complex. Howe (1910) records the quarry at Bothenhampton as having a '6 feet bed', which would account for the excellent ashlar cut from this quarry. The quarries known as Wanderwell are now a nature reserve renowned for its orchids, as well as a Regionally Important Geological Site. It is still possible to see how deep the workings must have been. In an old photograph in Bridport Museum the beds of shelly limestone are only about 3 centimetres thick in the upper part of the quarry, but thicken to about a metre lower down. The thin beds have been used for

Bothenhampton limekiln was cleaned in 1994. The old quarries are now a nature reserve known as Wanderwell, and it is not possible to see the quarry faces. However, it is so important historically, having provided excellent building stone for a large area of West Dorset, that it is designated as a Regionally Important Geological Site.

An estate map of 1884 includes three quarries on North Hill, Burton Bradstock. Only one remains visible at the end of the 20th century, as the other two have been filled with rubbish [© Dorset Archives Service ED PIT P4].

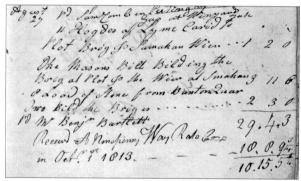

In the Shipton Gorge accounts for 1813-14 the masons bill for building the 'Brig at Plot and the Wier at Smakanz' is £3.11.6., while 8 loads of stone from Banton Quarr for the 'Brig' is £2.30. Banton is the local name for Bothenhampton [© Dorset Archives Service PE/SHG/SU1].

roofing and the thickest ones cut for ashlar. Hutchins records that 3200 tile stones were sold to Beaminster church for the roof in 1683, at a cost of £2.17s.0d.

Other beds have produced dressed stone and paving slabs. A small quarry can still be seen at Bothenhampton by following the footpath eastwards from Wanderwell along the ridge of Wych Hill. The beds are of varying thickness and drape over each other where the current has pushed banks of broken shells one over another.

The Surveyor's accounts for Shipton Gorge in 1813 regarding the building of a bridge, the Dorset History Centre record (PE/SHG/SU1) for August 27th

'11 hogdes (hogsheads) of Lyme car'd to Plot brig & Smakanz weir   £1. 2. 0.
The mason's bill bilding the brig at Plot & the weir at Smakanz   £3.11.6.
8 load of stone from Banton Quarr two bild the brig is £2. 3. 0.'

Specifications for the rebuilding of a house in East Street in 1834 show the wide choice of stone then available to the builders. (DRO/D30/3)

Cellar floor and walls – Bothenhampton stone – Forest Marble.
Walls above floor level of stone from Stoney Head quarry (Loders) – Inferior Oolite. [*This quarry closed when the A35 east of Bridport was re-aligned in 1975*].
Shop front storey to be faced with Portland Stone and the 2 upper storeys and parapet faced with Exbury brick [*why so far? Exbury is on Southampton Water*]
Hall floor of Portland stone.
Steps to cellar of Portland stone. 14 x 12 feet of cellar floor to be paved with Purbeck stone.

Portland stone coping on roof and 3 string courses of Portland stone, plus window cills, chimney pieces.
Drawing room chimney piece of Devon marble.
Pantry under hall floored with Bampton stone (Bothenhampton), with Portland stone washbasin.
Joseph & Frederick Galpin, builders.

The old cottages in Bothenhampton village are all built of Forest Marble, but Shipton Gorge village only uses it for foundations and the bridge and weir described above that were standing in water.

In Hutchins' *History of Dorset* it is recorded (II, 205) that the church in Allington was built in 1826-7 of Bothenhampton stone, and rendered in Roman cement. Charmouth parish church was rebuilt in 1836 with a foundation plinth of Forest Marble from Bothenhampton, a core of local rubble from the beach and facing of chert from Morcombelake. Beer stone and Ham Hill Stone have been used for the doorways and window mullions. The *Dorset County Chronicle* of 31st August 1865 reported that the new church at Eype was built of local stone from Bothenhampton.

Earlier Forest Marble masonry is not recorded in writing, but can be seen in the buildings themselves as far afield as Whitchurch Canonicorum, where it has been used in the west end of the south wall of the church. Asker Bridge, on the Allington side of Bridport and dated 1784 has an arch of Forest Marble. The foundations of the church, Shute's Farm and The Buildings in Symondsbury are of Forest Marble, supporting Inferior Oolite walls. The roof of Little Toller Farm was originally of Forest Marble 'tiles', but these were removed and used for a path.

Smaller quarries were dug at Swyre in New Lane, Puncknowle near Look Farm and Limekiln Hill at Bexington to provide building stone in the villages. Some of the quarries are still visible, though overgrown, and appear on nineteenth century maps.

At Burton Bradstock the fifteenth century Rookery Cottage is built of Forest Marble, while The Magnolias (thought to be originally a Tudor building) has been built of Forest Marble and Inferior Oolite. There are Forest Marble slabs as flooring in the kitchen. In the eighteenth century it was upgraded with a brick front and Blue Lias flagstones throughout the remainder of the ground floor. The seventeenth century Shadrach Farm, Ingram House, Graston House and other cottages are a mixture of Forest Marble and Inferior Oolite. A row of weavers cottages built in 1800 north of Mill

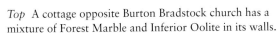

Top A cottage opposite Burton Bradstock church has a mixture of Forest Marble and Inferior Oolite in its walls.

Above The edges of broken shells can be seen in the plinth of Charmouth church, built in the 19th century of Forest Marble shelly limestone from Bothenhampton Q uarry.

Above right The surface of a piece of Forest Marble shelly limestone from Swyre. The flower-shaped shell is a crinoid plate [as seen through a handlens]. At Swyre the shells are cemented together with powdery calcite (micrite).

Right The Mill cottages south of Burton Bradstock church have Forest Marble limestone at the base of the wall, and Inferior Oolite with many brachiopods above.

House have Forest Marble in the lower courses and Inferior Oolite above. The Inferior Oolite has many brachiopods that fit the description by Buckman (1910) of the lowest bed in Larkfield Quarry. The Forest Marble could have come from North Hill, or a quarry on the Bredy Road; the Inferior Oolite from Southover and Larkfield quarries. Successive Ordnance Survey maps show that the Bredy Road quarry has been worked progressively further west between 1888 and the 1950's.

In Langton Herring a series of maps from the eighteenth into the nineteenth century shows how the open quarry area moved across the hillside as the stone was worked (see following page). Three Forest Marble quarries can be seen as 'waste' on a pre-1762 map showing the strip fields before enclosure. A fourth one appears on the tithe map drawn in 1837. The buildings in Langton Herring are a mixture of Forest Marble and Corallian limestone from a ridge well to the north. The Forest Marble blocks are all a sandy colour and it is difficult to differentiate between the shelly limestone and the sandstone. However, in

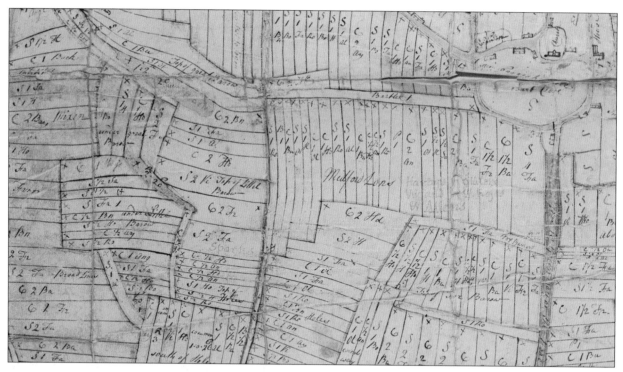

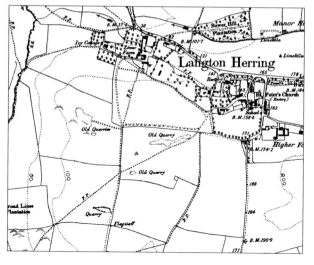

A series of three maps of Langton Herring showing how the fields and quarries changed over a hundred years.

Top An estate map drawn before 1762 shows the strip fields, with quarries marked as Waste [© Dorset County Archives. D SBS P4].

Above left The same three quarries appear on the tithe map of 1837, with the large enclosed fields. There is an additional large quarry in a field to the east of the earlier quarries, with a small one in the south-west corner of the same field [© Dorset County Archives. T LAH].

Above right On the Ordnance Survey map of 1888 the southern of the initial three quarries has disappeared, but the eastern quarry has extended.

the drystone walls near the old quarries the upright stones show the surface of the beds, with both types rich in sand and stained orange by iron.

At West Fleet a quarry in the Forest Marble provided stone for the fifteenth century parish church and sandstone roofing tiles. These have a ripple marked upper surface and therefore must have been deposited in shallow water. The grains of sand are cemented together with fine grained calcite and often there are trails left by small snails working through the sand. Some of these trails look like plaited hair snaking over the surface and are known as *Gyrochorte*.

A block of Forest Marble sandstone from a field wall near the quarries in Langton Herring. The small blocks in the buildings often contain shells.

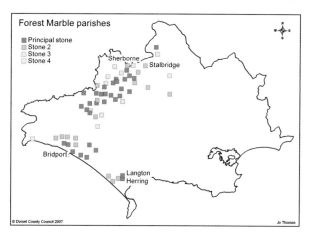

The church has thick slabs used as roofing tiles, the weight being evident in the splayed walls.

In the Bride Valley the villages are below the Chalk hills, close to the springs issuing from the Upper Greensand aquifer. In Litton Cheney the Forest Marble used in Brewery Cottage and Charity Farm would have come from Swyre or Punckowle. The Corallian limestone mixed with Forest Marble in Barges Farm (1707) was quarried at Baglake Farm, to the east of the village. The building at right angles to the road next to Brook Cottage has Forest Marble walls with Corallian quoins and an upper course of Chalk which must have been added in order to raise the roof.

Chalk block was quarried at Pins Knoll chalkpit which was approximately 15 metres (50 feet) deep and was used as the parish pit. Not all the Chalk would have been used for building. In this often wet valley it would also have been used for roadstone. Chalk was used for the walls of seventeenth century Glebe Cottage and Myrtle Cottage (1700), in both cases above a Forest Marble plinth. Both Portland and Purbeck limestone from Portesham Quarry have been used in the tower and porch of the church, whose walls are mostly Corallian limestone, but include some Forest Marble.

In Little Bredy the Corallian limestone, local flint, Lower Purbeck from Portesham and cob are used in the cottages, but the 1850 part of the church and the stable block at Bridehead are built of Caen stone from France. The mix of building materials in Long Bredy is similar to Litton Cheney. Baglake Farm is actually in the parish of Long Bredy and while the house is built of fine Corallian ashlar the barn is a striking combination of Corallian limestone in the lower half and Chalk block above.

Northern Area

South of Sherborne the Forest Marble quarries from Lillington Hill to Longburton were used for the Sherborne Castle Estate, not only for building walls but also for roofing tiles and flooring. The exterior walls of the nineteenth century addition to the stable block are of Forest Marble shelly limestone, while the older exterior is of Inferior Oolite and the courtyard face of Ham Hill Stone. Howe (1910) records quarries at Long Burton, '12 to 15 feet, in beds from 2 to 9 inches thick', and at Bowden '20 feet of very shelly and slightly oolitic limestone, the so-called Bowden Marble'.

Thin sandy beds with ripple marks on the upper

Sherborne Deer Park wall, by the Haydon gate, has been built of Forest Marble shelly limestone and thin sandstone blocks from quarries within the park.

The barn at Haydon Manor Farm is built of thin Forest Marble sandstone blocks, with some shelly limestone.

Forest Marble sandstone tiles on an outhouse at West Hall, Folke.

surface have been used as roofing tiles over a large area of West Dorset. Where the sandstone occurs in isolated patches within the clays, these were collected by hand from shallow delves. The sandstone has also been found between the beds of shelly limestone. The sandstone tiles from the quarries at Longburton, on Lillington Hill and within the deer park have been used for roofing in Sherborne for the Almshouses near the Abbey and other listed buildings, as well as many cottages in the villages, and West Hall and the Manor in Folke. The extensive outcrop of sandstone in Stalbridge was used for building the older houses, and provided roofing tiles that appear thicker than those from Longburton.

Very thin shelly limestone beds are also used for roofing but on lifting them I find that for the same thickness they are heavier. In Sherborne and Yetminster both Forest Marble shelly limestone and Ham Hill Stone have been cut for use as roofing tiles. From the ground it is difficult to tell the difference in weathered stone, but a broken edge should show the colour. Forest Marble limestone is dark grey, Ham Hill Stone is orange. Like Ham Hill Stone, the shell fragments in Forest Marble are all lying flat and packed tightly together. However, the fragments of shell are larger and include bivalves, brachiopods, gastropods and crinoid plates (circular, up to 3 centimetres diameter with a hole in the middle, or star-shaped). The dark grey colour is caused by the darker shells, in contrast to the orange caused by the presence of oxidised iron in the Ham Hill Stone.

Several of the Purbeck Marble pillars in the Lady

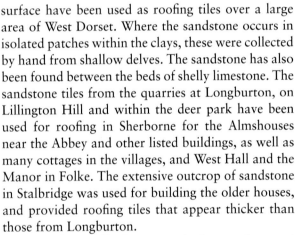

Chapel of Sherborne Abbey were replaced with Forest Marble shelly limestone during the nineteenth century. They appear the same colour, but do not include the *Viviparus* gastropod so characteristic of the Purbeck. The sandstone quarried from West Hill has been used for cobblestones in the Abbey precinct, and has also been identified in Shaftesbury and Southampton. The cobbles, or setts, were brick-shaped pieces of stone turned on edge, so that the wear was taken across the grain of the stone and there was less danger of the road becoming slippery. In Longburton the oldest quarry was on the eastern side of the road, to the north of the village.

Holy Trinity church at Leweston was built from these quarries in 1616. The western quarry was opened in the mid twentieth century, and a great deal

Forest Marble shelly limestone quarried at Corscombe has been squashed into a closer texture by fault movements.

A block of Forest Marble shelly limestone in Longburton church.

This block of Forest Marble in Yetminster church shows a change from shelly, sand rich limestone at the top to sandstone with few shells at the bottom. The stone used in the village is variable in this way in all the buildings.

of stone was crushed to create a runway at the nearby airfield at Henstridge during the Second World War.

Although the grey, crystalline, shelly limestone of the Forest Marble is instantly recognisable throughout West Dorset, the detail can subtly change. Forest Marble from Halstock has been used in Corscombe, though a quarry was recently opened in a small fault-bounded outcrop in Corscombe itself. This proved exceptionally strong because of the pressure of the fault movement, which appears to have caused recrystallisation. Unfortunately it was only a small deposit.

In Longburton the dark shelly nature of the limestone means that the cottages along the main street are uniformly grey, giving a rather gloomy appearance. In Melbury Osmond, however, the street itself is less formal, adding twists and turns and much more vegetation. The village is built on a foundation of Cornbrash, which sticks out like the witch's shoes from under several cottages. The back garden of Rock Cottage appears sunken, suggesting that there was a quarry behind the house. This probably went into the Forest Marble through the Cornbrash. The deeds of Rock Cottage and Rock House, (DRO/D707/T1) list the Linscombe family as masons from 1696 to the early nineteenth century.

There were thirteen quarries in the parish, nine with Cornbrash on the surface, probably with Forest Marble underneath. The Forest Marble was used for building, the Cornbrash for limeburning. All the cottages are of Forest Marble, and the church has a fifteenth century west tower of the same stone. The remainder of the church was rebuilt in 1745 of Ham Hill Stone.

The church in Melbury Sampford parish has been less altered. Built in 1440 of Forest Marble, it was improved in 1874 and has Ham Hill Stone dressings. Melbury House was started in 1530 for Sir Giles Strangways with an octagonal tower of Ham Hill Stone, three wings of Ham Hill Stone being added later. Hutchins records that 3000 loads of stone were required. In 1692 Watson remodelled the north and south fronts and created a new east façade, in brick faced with Ham Hill Stone. White Portland stone was used for quoins and keystones. There is a turreted Garden House of Forest Marble.

Forest Marble is used in Evershot, with some Chalk block. Evershot pit has been dug through the lowest Chalk into the soft Foxmould of the Upper Greensand. This sand was used in the mortar.

Yetminster has been built of Forest Marble that varies between shelly and sandy with some shells. This more varied stone gives a warmer appearance to the village, in contrast to Longburton. The Forest Marble in this area sometimes contains small patches of orange clay, a characteristic which can also been seen in the cottages of Leigh and Chetnole, suggesting that their stone came from Yetminster quarry. The Yetminster quarry was at Quarr Close 'in which it is lawfull for the tennants to dig and to carry away at all times such stone as they shall need to build or repair their houses'. The surface rock here is Cornbrash, but the quarry was very deep and well into the Forest Marble Formation. This is typical of many parish quarries. They were seen as a common resource for

Above Upbury Farm in Yetminster, built of local Forest Marble with Ham Hill Stone dressings and Forest Marble stone tiles on the roof.

Left Boyles School in Yetminster, built of the local Forest Marble with Ham Hill Stone windows and doorway.

The roofs of the houses have the somewhat heavy appearance of the sandstone, like that in East Fleet. Later quarries in the shelly limestone have provided building material for nineteenth century building.

CORNBRASH

The Cornbrash limestone is rarely used for building, since it tends to be rubbly, but the lowest bed is massive and strong enough for use. It is generally cream coloured, but in different locations the

A view of Stalbridge Forest Marble Quarry in 2006.

the village rather than a commercial commodity owned by one family. Cross House in Leigh has a few courses of Cornbrash on the roadside. Their rubbly appearance contrasts with the square or thin rectangular blocks of Forest Marble.

There were many small quarries between Bishop's Caundle and Stalbridge whose stone was used for vernacular buildings and for bridges on the tributaries of the Stour. In the small bridges within the Stour valley the blocks of Forest Marble are weathered and covered in lichen. It is therefore difficult to differentiate between the shelly and sandy beds, but a bridge engineer assures me that many of them are from the sandstone beds. In Stalbridge itself an outcrop of the sandstone in Stalbridge Park has been used for the older buildings and for garden walls.

Most of the older buildings in Stalbridge are of Forest Marble sandstone from a large outcrop within Stalbridge Park. Nineteenth century buildings are of shelly limestone from deeper in the local quarries.

building stone bed has been described as faintly blue or pink. The Cornbrash limestone has been quarried in Stalbridge, but it appears to have been used for only one building. The wall round Stalbridge Park has been built of stone from the nearest quarry, and as there were several Cornbrash, at least one Forest Marble sandstone and several Forest Marble limestone quarries, it changes character on the way round. Accounts of the sale of stone from Stalbridge quarries, both Cornbrash and Forest Marble, between 1780 and 1854, are lodged in the Dorset History Centre, in the papers of the Marquess of Anglesey. To quote from *The Stalbridge Inheritance*, by Irene Jones: 'The first Estate Rental Book for 1781 contains an entry for the sale of 30 loads of stone to the Surveyors of the Highway and 3 loads to George Lemon at 1s per load. In 1789 Robert James . . . was paid for the carriage of stone to repair the Park Wall, Samuel Seymour, mason, being paid the sum of £74.15s.4d. for repairs to the Park Wall from January to November.'

Stone from the Fleet and Chickerell quarries was used in the old village of Chickerell for houses as well as field walls. The old church in Chickerell (1260) was built of Forest Marble sandstone, with some shelly Forest Marble and some Cornbrash. The porch was rebuilt in 1722 using old materials, and has a Lower Purbeck archway. Lower Purbeck was also used for the windows. In 1834 a north aisle was built in which the Cornbrash predominates: it is not wearing well. Prospect Place, a pair of cottages near the church, was built in 1869 with a mixture of Forest Marble sandstone and Cornbrash. The remains of a Cornbrash limestone quarry can still be seen next to the road at East Fleet, where the stone was used for East Fleet Farm. Cornbrash was also used in Radipole, near Weymouth, both in the church and in the old manor house.

Top Chickerell is one of the few villages where Cornbrash is used for building. The house on the corner of West Street has rough blocks of pale Cornbrash limestone with a few thinner slabs of darker Forest Marble sandstone.

Centre Cornbrash limestone is rarely used for building, but often burnt for lime. There are several limekilns in Bradford Lane, Longburton that burnt Cornbrash from the nearby fields, but were built of Forest Marble limestone from the northern side of the village.

Bottom A pair of nineteenth century cottages near Chickerell church is built of Cornbrash limestone with some blocks of Forest Marble sandstone.

CHAPTER FIVE

Corallian Limestones

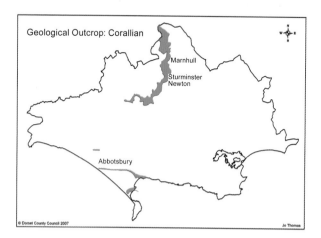

Geological Outcrop: Corallian

Marnhull

Sturminster
Newton

Abbotsbury

© Dorset County Council 2007   Jo Thomas

GEOLOGY

For about eight or nine million years after the shallow water Cornbrash limestone, the sea became deeper again and the Oxford Clay was deposited on the sea floor. Then for over a million years sea level fluctuated in depth, probably due to the opening of the north Atlantic and the regular movement of the continental shelf.

The Corallian Formation is a classic offshore depositional cyclic sequence of limestones, clays and sandstones that has been studied in detail on the Dorset coast near Osmington and in the north throughout its outcrop from Bourton to Mappowder. As knowledge has progressed the number of cycles identified has varied from three to nine, though it is thought that the northern area may have been nearer the centre of a marine basin, thus preserving more cycles of sedimentation than the shallower south. These depositional cycles are of clay deposited furthest from land in deeper water, sand nearer to shore and limestone in the shallowest water. Repetition of the cycles indicates that the offshore shelf was subject to rhythmic changes in sea level. The succession of fossil ammonites found in the

limestones indicates that these beds are about 156 million years old. Oysters and other bivalves occur in several of the limestones and clays, but the main building stone has very few fossils, its characteristic one being *Nucleolites scutatus,* a small echinoid, or sea urchin.

The most important building stone was named originally from its cliff exposure as the Osmington Oolite. In Abbotsbury the stone is a warm orange in colour and was quarried from Chapel and Linton Hills. Blocks could be cut from the lowest and thickest beds up to 1 metre x 60 cm x 30 cm. The ooliths in the limestone are large enough to see with the naked eye, in a matrix of crystalline calcite (sparite) and fine micrite. The colour is dependent on the amount of disseminated iron within the limestone. It is often

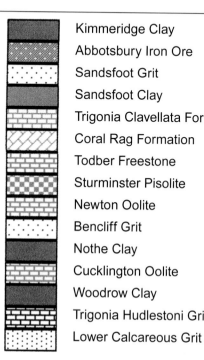

	Kimmeridge Clay
	Abbotsbury Iron Ore
	Sandsfoot Grit
	Sandsfoot Clay
	Trigonia Clavellata Formation
	Coral Rag Formation
	Todber Freestone
	Sturminster Pisolite
	Newton Oolite
	Bencliff Grit
	Nothe Clay
	Cucklington Oolite
	Woodrow Clay
	Trigonia Hudlestoni Grit
	Lower Calcareous Grit

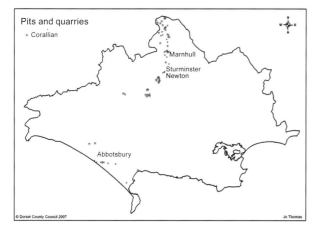

Corallian Todber Freestone is an oolitic limestone with micrite cement. From Birds Quarry, Todber (as seen through a handlens).

blue when freshly quarried, but the iron oxidises to produce the orange seen in buildings.

In North Dorset this part of the Formation has been subdivided so that the main building stone is named the Todber Freestone. This is an oolitic sparite limestone with shell fragments, occurring in beds from 30 centimetres to 1 metre thick. The beds are similar in texture, the ooliths being visible to the naked eye, with some sparite cement but mostly fine-grained calcite filling the pores. The porosity is therefore low. The colour of the limestone varies from place to place, being cream to orange. The best building stone in Marnhull is pale cream, which hardens and whitens on exposure. It is slightly darker at Todber, where the beds in the quarries drape over one another as if the oolite was in banks being moved by a marine current towards the south east. Lower in the sequence, the Newton Oolite is flaggy medium grained oolitic limestone with micrite, in beds that

total up to 3 metres, seen in the quarry at Fifehead Neville and used in the church. The Cucklington Oolite above the Todber Freestone in the sequence, is a reddish brown sandy oolitic sparite limestone quarried north of Todber and at Cucklington.

LANDSCAPE

The Corallian rocks outcrop in two main areas of Dorset; in the north from northwest of Gillingham southwards to Lyon's Gate and in the south on each limb of the Weymouth Anticline, from Abbotsbury to Osmington Mills and from Wyke Regis to Sandsfoot Castle.

The northern outcrop runs north to south from the county border where it is cut off by the unconformity (younger rocks covering older ones with a long time gap in between) with the Cretaceous, creating a low ridge from Bourton to Sturminster Newton. Here it meets the scarp face of the Chalk and then continues in the low ground north of the Chalk Downs through Fifehead Neville and Mappowder. West of Mappowder it is again covered by the Cretaceous unconformity, or has been eroded away. Although cut by many faults, the outcrop north of Sturminster Newton creates a low hill which in places is accentuated by the proximity of the River Stour cutting into the Oxford Clay beneath, especially on the western side of Sturminster Newton.

The southern outcrops dip respectively north at Abbotsbury and south at Wyke Regis, on either limb of the Weymouth anticline, creating steeper and more noticeable hills than in North Dorset. The northern ridge runs from Chapel and Linton Hills at Abbotsbury to the sea at Osmington Mills. The southern ridge is mostly built up, but the shape of the hill is clearly visible above the Oxford and Kimmeridge Clay lowlands either side.

QUARRYING AND USE IN BUILDINGS

In the Blackmore Vale the most important quarries were between Marnhull and Todber. The best quality Freestone (Todber Freestone) was quarried at Marnhull and was an almost white oolitic limestone, free of fossils. Between Marnhull and Todber several large quarries in the Todber Freestone have been in use since medieval times and possibly earlier, as there are Roman remains. There are still three working quarries in this area. The upper beds in the present

quarries have a micrite cement between the ooliths and the lower best beds have a sparite cement.

The Todber Freestone thins and dies out both north and south, so that other villages use limestones from different parts of the Formation. Cucklington Oolite is a dark orange/brown oolitic limestone and was quarried north of Marnhull at Great Down Lane and on the hill above Buckhorn Weston. It can be recognised in many of the northern villages. Gillingham church is built of Corallian ashlar.

Hinton St. Mary had its own quarries in the Todber Freestone. The White Horse Inn is built of well-dressed Corallian stone, smoothly finished, but uncoursed, with a stone roof. The church is built of Corallian ashlar, with Upper Greensand from Shaftesbury in the lower courses and the west doorway. The Manor barn next to the church and the thatched Yeomans Wake Cottage are of local stone. The raised footway from the church to the inn is of large slabs of stone with a 'wavy' or uneven surface that appear to be of local stone, probably one of the sandstones in the Corallian Group. This paving occurs in several villages in the Blackmore Vale.

Sturminster Newton has been built on a bluff of Corallian limestone. In the nineteenth century the Great Western Railway cut through almost all of the Corallian beds to take the trains through the town from one part of the Stour valley to the other. Houses in the town may have been built of stone from Todber or Marnhull, but the settlement of Newton had its own quarries and the buildings there are of noticeably coarser stone. The mill above Town Bridge is partly of Corallian limestone, but the foundations that stand in the River Stour are of Upper Greensand from Shaftesbury. The Corallian limestone is not suitable to stand in water. The quarry at Fifehead Neville had about 2 metres thickness of building stone similar to the stone at Newton, a coarse-grained cream coloured limestone with occasional fossils.

At Todber the fossil-rich *Trigonia clavellata*

Top The building stone beds in the Corallian Todber Freestone at Birds Quarry are each about 0.75m thick and can be cut as ashlar.

Middle The barn near the church in Hinton St. Mary has Corallian Todber Freestone walls with Upper Greensand sandstone buttresses.

Bottom Church Farm in Sturminster Newton is built of Corallian limestone with a foundation plinth of more damp-resistant Forest Marble.

Beds are unsuitable for building because the fossils create points of weakness in the stone. The Todber Freestone is almost free of fossils. However the Todber Freestone has died out further south at Mappowder and the 'fossil beds', as the *Trigonia* beds are known, have been used in the church. In the tower the stone is well preserved but some of the later work on the porch is not weathering so well. This may be due to the type of mortar which has been used. Lime mortar should be used with limestone, not cement.

Corallian limestone has been used throughout the Stour valley above Blandford. North of Fifehead Magdalen the Cucklington Oolite is used along with better quality stone from Marnhull. Most of the houses in Marnhull and Stour Provost are built of dressed stone, using cream or white limestone. In many of the villages there is also an occasional use of Upper Greensand from Shaftesbury and Melbury Abbas. Higher Farm at Margaret Marsh is built of Corallian limestone, probably brought down the Stour valley from Marnhull or Todber, with some Greensand in the lower courses.

Most of the more prestigious houses in this valley are of ashlar from Marnhull and Todber, for example the manor house in Hammoon (sixteenth century) and the main part of Stepleton House (mid seventeenth century). Fiddleford Manor (1374-80) has a mixture of local Corallian limestone, some fine ashlar from Marnhull (sixteenth century) and some larger blocks of Upper Greensand. Hanford House (1604-23) has been built of ashlar from Marnhull which is a very pale cream, over Upper Greensand foundations. The superb original entrance is in a central courtyard, roofed over in Edwardian times, which has preserved the fine carving from further weathering. Many of the mullions were replaced with Bath Stone at the same time, and other Edwardian buildings of brick have Bath Stone dressings, though there is some Corallian limestone in the stable block. The eleventh century church at Iwerne Stepleton is of Corallian limestone rubble. Sutton Waldron has one house in which Corallian limestone has been used on one

Top Iris Cottage, Marnhull has smoothfaced blocks of Corallian Todber Freestone from the Marnhull quarries.

Middle Street Farm in Marnhull was built of small blocks of 'Marnhull' stone (Todber Freestone from Marnhull).

Bottom Hammoon Manor was built of Corallian ashlar from quarries in Marnhull where the Todber Freestone was a paler colour than at Todber.

St. Catherine's Chapel was built in the 14th century from a quarry on the eastern side of its own hill.

Seventeenth and eighteenth century cottages in Abbotsbury have re-used the stone originally dug for the Abbey. The orange stone is Corallian Osmington Oolite limestone. The occasional white block is Portland limestone from Portesham farm quarry that had been used as ashlar facing for some parts of the Abbey.

wall and Upper Greensand on another. Locally made brick is also an important feature of the villages on the road below the Chalk downs. Both the Gault and Kimmeridge clays have been used for brickmaking.

South of the River Stour at Shillingstone the Corallian limestone is used with some flint in the cottages. In the church, which is of Saxon origin, a Norman window (1090) is of Corallian limestone, while the tower (1450) is of Upper Greensand. Nineteenth century and recent work includes flint and Bath and Portland limestones. In Child Okeford on the north of the river a considerable amount of brick is used and the Corallian is mixed with Upper Greensand and some Chalk block. The fifteenth century tower of the church is of Upper Greensand, the remainder of the church being mostly flint. The Olde House has some Chalk block on the front of the house, as well as Upper Greensand, some Corallian limestone, brick, flint and a small patch of timber frame. At Fontmell Parva House the majority of the house is locally made brick, but Corallian limestone has been used for dressings.

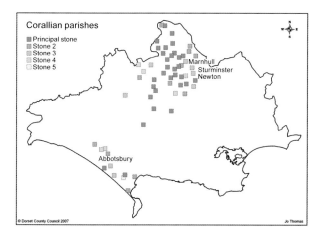

In South Dorset the Osmington Oolite (equivalent to the Todber Freestone) has been extensively quarried in Abbotsbury where the oolitic limestone has more fossils than in Marnhull and Todber. Although only a fragment of the great Benedictine abbey still stands, we know that it was originally built of Corallian limestone from the east side of Chapel Hill, where the old quarry is now overgrown with trees. All the beds were used, the poorer quality as fill between the inner and outer skins of the walls. The Tithe Barn, the dairy and St. Catherine's chapel on the hill are all of the best quality orange Corallian ashlar. However,

Above Oddens Quarry, at the foot of Linton Hill, Abbotsbury has many beds of oolitic limestone (Osmington Oolite) that can all be used for building. The thin beds provide paving slabs, those about 30 cm thick provide 'rubble' for cottage or boundary walls and the thickest (about 1m) can be cut as ashlar for more important buildings. This was a nineteenth century quarry, now reopened.

Below The Corallian limestone ridge south east of Abbotsbury village shows the northward dip of the beds and the south facing scarp. Oddens Quarry is at the foot of the near end of the hill.

Above The church in Langton Herring has used several of the building stones available locally. The south side of the chancel has a wall of Corallian limestone that could have come from Rodden hill to the north of the village, with Lower Purbeck Cypris Freestone blocks from the Ridgeway quarries round the window.

Below The tower of Litton Cheney church is built of a mixture of the white laminated Lower Purbeck Cypris Freestones from the Ridgeway quarries and Corallian limestone from Baglake Farm to the east of the village.

the ashlar in the gatehouse is of white Portland age stone from Portesham quarry. The same stone has been used in an addition to the dairy and can be seen in the fourteenth century church. To the right of the west door several blocks of badly weathered white stone show the texture to be like small pellets of lime, with a few bivalve fossils. The crenellations above the north wall of the church are of Ham Hill Stone, which weathers to a dark brown. In the porch is an effigy of a 13th century abbot in Purbeck Marble.

When the Abbey was demolished the stone was re-used in the village. Other beds of Corallian limestone from these quarries have also been used in the village buildings. They are orange to brown in colour and more sandy than oolitic. These beds are immediately beneath the Abbotsbury Ironstone, which underlies the village and part of the hill to the north. In the nineteenth century quarries were opened on Linton Hill for further building, and the largest (Oddens Wood quarry) is being re-opened at the beginning of the twenty-first century for repairs to the historic buildings. Here there are 4 metres of thin beds underlain by three beds each around a metre thick that could be cut for ashlar. Only a few blocks of the white Portland stone can be seen reused in the village buildings. However, another white stone from Portesham, laminated and of a fine powdery texture, is present in several houses. This is the lower Purbeck limestone which was quarried from many shallow delves on the hill from Portesham Farm eastwards.

The outcrop of Corallian limestone on Linton Hill extends eastward, so that Rodden and Langton Herring also have buildings with some Corallian. In Langton Herring the Corallian is mixed with Forest Marble sandy and shelly limestone. Wyke Regis and the old part of Weymouth are built on the high ground of the Corallian limestones. Sandsfoot Castle has lost most of its ashlar exterior, but the rubble core remaining was taken from the local cliffs of Osmington Oolite and *Trigonia Clavellata* Beds. Although the Corallian limestones are present east of Weymouth, the lower Purbeck limestones have been the preferred building stones.

The use of Corallian limestone in Litton Cheney has already been described in the chapter on Forest Marble. The outcrop here is the result of a fold bringing the Corallian to the surface on either side of a syncline (a downfold with younger rocks preserved in the middle) immediately south of a fault running east-west through the parish.

Portland Freestone

GEOLOGY

For ten million years the continental shelf sank again and the deep-water Kimmeridge Clay was deposited. As the sea began to shallow at about 145 million years ago the deposition of the sediments that became the Portland Beds began with the Portland Sand, much of which is now a lime-rich sandstone As shallowing continued, lime mud was deposited containing many nodules of chert formed of the silica remains of sponges or radiolarians. This has become the Cherty Series. In the shallowest sea the Freestones were formed, of ooliths, pellets or shell sand.

The three quarrying areas produce Portland Freestone of different character, due to the differing environments of deposition. In the Isle of Portland a submarine swell area is thought to have formed due to the rise of a salt dome. In shallow water, about 15 to 20 feet deep (5 to 6 metres), ooliths were formed and created a marine dune complex.

The main freestone beds, known as the Base Bed and the Whit Bed, both about 2 metres thick, have little shell content. During lithification the ooliths were attacked by stone-eating microbes, which left holes later filled with sparite. The freestones are grain supported, and both have little natural cement. Their porosity allows the stone to dry out quickly after rain, and they are therefore durable. They are separated by limestones with more shells that may have resulted from quieter conditions.

The general sequence on the Isle of Portland is:

ROACH: Oolitic limestone, with many empty moulds of bivalves and gastropods.
WHIT BED: Oolitic limestone, the best freestone. Ooliths have been replaced by crystalline calcite, and the grains support each other, without a matrix, creating a porous stone. There are some broken shells, which stand proud after weathering.
FLINTY BED: Limestone full of chert.
CURF: Soft, chalky limestone.

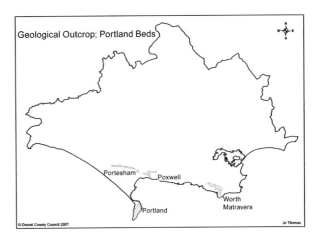

Geological Outcrop; Portland Beds

Portesham
Poxwell
Worth Matravers
Portland

© Dorset County Council 2007   Jo Thomas

BASE BED ROACH: Shelly oolitic limestone.
BASE BED: Good freestone with few shells, soft, white, oolitic.

The Base Bed is the softer of the two and more easily worked, but is thought to be of poorer quality, though it is almost exclusively used for headstones, which are upright and therefore vulnerable to weathering. The Whit Bed contains a scattering of large broken

A freshly cut piece of Roach Bed Portland Freestone at Bowers Quarry, Portland. The cavities are in the shape of the gastropods (Portland Screw - *Aptyxiella portlandicus*) and bivalves ('osses 'eads -*Myophorella incurva*) that have dissolved away.

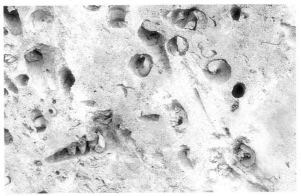

Base Bed Portland Freestone used as a headstone in St. George's churchyard, Reforne, Portland.

Portland limestone at Portesham has a finer texture than on the Isle of Portland. It includes more broken shells, and the matrix is pellets rather than ooliths. The pellets would have been the excreta of marine animals like shrimps who ingested lime mud, extracted organic matter as food and excreted the inert lime mud as pellets. [This cut piece from Portesham quarry has been etched with dilute acid – actual size].

bivalves and so has a rougher appearance. Above the Whit Bed is another oolitic freestone which originally contained many gastropods (the Portland Screw – *Aptyxiella portlandica*) and bivalves ('osses 'eds – *Laevitrigonia* and *Myophorella*) which have been dissolved away leaving shaped cavities. This is the Roach, often used nowadays for sea defences, and in the past for fortifications such as Nothe Fort and Hurst Castle. Many of the buildings on the Isle of Portland, including St. George, Reforne, are of the Roach. Patch reefs of the algae *Solenopora* grew up on the edges of the oolite shoals, and this has been used for decorative work.

At Portesham and Upwey the fine grained chalky white limestones formed in a quiet lagoon behind the oolitic dune complex. Quarries at Chalbury and Poxwell produce limestone of similar texture. Examination of the texture of the uppermost freestone at Portesham shows that the limestone is made of faecal pellets with some large bivalve shells. Below this bed is a chert rich bed and then two more beds of limestone, the lowest of which yielded a specimen of the ammonite *Titanites giganteus*.

The sequence still visible at Portesham is:
Two 0.5 metre beds of fine grained limestone with many bivalve shells, some replaced with crystalline calcite.
Three beds totalling 2 metres of limestone with chert nodules.
Two 0.5 metre beds of chalky white limestone, no fossils except for *Titanites giganteus* found 1999.

In the Isle of Purbeck the Portland Freestone Beds formed in an open shelf sea that was slightly deeper than the Isle of Portland dune complex. The lowest bed quarried from the cliffs is the Under Freestone, which is the best quality stone and comes from beds about 2 metres thick. Above the Under Freestone were four beds of limestone containing oysters and some *Titanites* ammonites, with a chert-rich bed at the top. The Pond Freestone, also about 2 metres thick, was quarried in galleries higher in the cliff. Both freestones are shell-sand limestones with occasional oolitic layers or scattered ooliths. There is very little sparite cement, and the freestone has good porosity. The cliff quarries continued in work until the 1930's. The only quarry working for building stone at present is St. Aldhelm's Head Quarry, where the Pond Freestone is the lowest bed worked. Above is the *Titanites* or Blue Bed known as the Spangle which contains bivalve fossils replaced by calcite crystals. The freestones thin westwards, and the Under Freestone is not worked at St. Aldhelm's. The Spangle has been used recently for decorative cladding inside buildings.

QUARRYING ON PORTLAND

Portland limestones are the best known of the building stones quarried in Dorset, because they have been used in prestigious buildings in many cities, including Dublin, Cardiff and London. It was quarried from the Isle of Portland, the cliffs of the Isle of Purbeck and from the Ridgeway above Weymouth. Early quarrying was done entirely by manpower, using pickaxes to open spaces between the beds on the bedding planes, and taking advantage

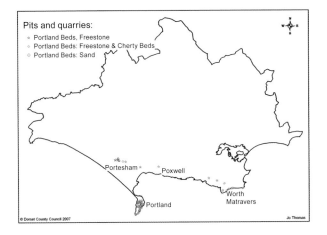

Pits and quarries:
- Portland Beds, Freestone
- Portland Beds: Freestone & Cherty Beds
- Portland Beds: Sand

Portesham
Poxwell
Portland
Worth Matravers

© Dorset County Council 2007   Jo Thomas

of vertical joints to lever out blocks of stone.

The Isle is a Royal Manor and fees have been paid to the Crown for centuries. This has given historians the opportunity to follow the progress of the quarrying. In the fourteenth century stone was exported to Exeter for the Cathedral, and about 50 years later to London for the royal palace of Westminster. In Queen Elizabeth I's reign there is a record of the payments required and the arrangements for quarrying and erecting of piers with cranes or sheers for shipping of stone. It was in the reign of James I that Inigo Jones built the Banqueting Hall in Whitehall, and of Charles II that Christopher Wren used Portland Stone to rebuild St. Paul's and the city churches. By 1702 Portland stone was being used by Wren to build Greenwich Hospital.

In 1791 John Smeaton recorded his visit to the Portland quarries to select stone for his Eddystone Lighthouse: 'When the merchantable blocks are cleared of the cap the quarrymen proceed to cross-cut the large flats which are laid bare with wedges. The beds being thus cut into distinct lumps the quarryman, with a tool cooled a 'kevel', which is at one end a hammer and at the other an axe, whose edge is so short or narrow that it approaches towards the shape of a pick, by a repetition of sturdy blows soon reduces a piece of stone, by his eye, to the largest square figure which it will admit.'

In 1908 the Victoria History recorded that blocks of from 10 to 12 tons could be obtained. Also that formerly stones were moved down the hill 'by large wooden trollies with solid wheels of wood, drawn by a team of horses, three behind, two abreast, and one following – the three behind operating as a drag.' The hill down to the sea is exceedingly steep! The Merchants' Railway was built in 1826 when

thousands of tons were being quarried and shipped. In the late nineteenth century large quantities of stone were used to build the breakwaters that have created Portland Harbour.

On the Purbeck cliffs quarrying could be undertaken horizontally, working gradually into the cliff. In this way galleries were opened up in the useful bed, leaving pillars of stone to hold up the roof. At Seacombe the main galleries are in the Under Freestone, with more galleries in the Pond Freestone near the top of the cliff. At Winspit the galleries are only in the Under Freestone. The Ridgeway quarries were worked into the sides of the hills, with the Portland Freestone being quarried below the Lower Purbeck Cypris Freestones.

On the Isle of Portland the quarries were worked downward into the top of the Island, having removed the Lower Purbeck overburden. Using pickaxes and levers, the stone was cut out by hand and then raised by cranes from the deep pits. With the spoil being piled up behind the working, the deep cuts in the old quarries seem to leave very little room to work. The quarries working today are large and open enough to allow the use of machinery to extract the stone. Blocks are sawn with a chain-saw attached to a platform on top of the stone, so that a large slice is cut vertically, using water to lubricate the cut. The block is then undercut and a forklift used to remove it to the workshop.

Once the stone was taken out of the quarry, it had to be split or cut. A line of wedge-shaped holes was chiselled along the top of a block, into which a wedge (the plug) with two strips of metal (the feathers) was hammered until the stone split. This method was still used in the 1930's. However, the introduction of frame saws and water power in the seventeenth century made it easier to cut the stone. In the twentieth century electricity is used to drive reciprocating and circular saws with diamond tipped or tungsten teeth.

LANDSCAPE

The Isle of Portland is the remnant of the shallow dipping southern limb of the Weymouth anticline (an upfold caused by earth movements). Much of the Kimmeridge Clay below the Portland Limestone and Sand Formations has been eroded away to form Weymouth Bay. The Portland Sand forms the western cliffs, with the limestones above, dipping south and

A 12th century gatepier at Abbotsbury Abbey is deeply weathered. Most of the Portland Freestone from Portesham Quarry, previously used as ashlar in the Abbey, has been re-used in the village buildings.

slightly east. The lowest Purbeck Beds cover the Portland Freestones over most of the Isle.

From above Portesham to Upwey the steeply dipping northern limb of the Weymouth anticline has outcrops of the Portland Freestone, often topped by Lower Purbeck limestone, so that both were quarried in the same place. They form a prominent ridge, with the scarp slope facing south. North east of Weymouth small scale folds and faults have created small hills such as Chalbury and the Poxwell Pericline where both the Portland Freestone and the Lower Purbeck have been quarried. The Poxwell Pericline is a clear boat shape on the hills bisected by the main road.

In the Isle of Purbeck, from St. Aldhelm's Head to Durlston Head, the cliffs are in the Portland Limestone Series, with the Cherty Beds at sea level and the Freestones above. The Freestones were quarried for centuries, the Pond Freestone and the Under Freestone being cut from galleries worked into the cliff face. As the galleries undermined the rising hill above, the floors of the quarries were piled with waste and fallen rock – as at Winspit, Seacombe, Dancing Ledge and Tilly Whim. Some galleries remain open, but can collapse without warning. At Dancing Ledge the gallery openings have been closed with grilles to protect the resident bats. Two quarries have been cut into the sides of steep combes near the coast. The St. Aldhelm's Head quarry produces building stone, and Swanworth quarry produces roadstone from both the Freestones and the Cherty Beds underneath. All the combes are topped with Purbeck Limestone dipping slightly north, so that the seaward facing slope above the cliffs is the scarp face of the Purbeck Limestone.

QUARRYING AND USE IN BUILDING

Ridgeway

Portland limestone from the Ridgeway quarries has been used in a wide area of West Dorset. Excavations were made into the sides of hills, so that hand working took advantage of gravity to remove blocks of stone. It is found in buildings as early as the fourteenth century, and continued in work until the late nineteenth century.

The condition of Portesham (SY609860), Chalbury (SY693837) and Poxwell (SY743835) quarries suggests that it was used occasionally in the twentieth century.

Stone from Portesham Quarry was used for the abbey in Abbotsbury, where the ruined Outer Gateway (fourteenth century) on the road to the Swannery is built of the highest bed identified in

An advertisement in the *Dorset County Chronicle* for 1889 shows the price of Portland and Purbeck stone from Portesham.

the quarry. The extreme weathering here, and in the west wall of the nearby church, shows the pelleted matrix and large bivalves replaced by calcite. It appears to have been used for the facing ashlar of the abbey buildings, and has been re-used in some of the cottages. It can also be seen at Cerne Abbas. Both abbeys were Benedictine foundations.

The Tudor manor house at Athelhampton is recorded to have used Portesham stone, but the main walls are of Lower Purbeck limestones. Because the two different limestones were quarried in the same place, here and in Purbeck, the location of the source rather than its geological name was used in contemporary records, or those of architectural historians.

Waddon Manor (17th & 18th centuries) is built of the Portland limestone from the hill above, and Corton Farm (sixteenth and seventeenth centuries) uses both the Portland and Purbeck stones. Hardy's Monument was built of ashlar from Portesham quarry in 1844 to commemorate Thomas Masterman Hardy – Nelson's captain. In the nineteenth century stone was carried by rail from Portesham quarry and the remains of a tramway down the hill are still visible.

An advertisement in the *Dorset County Chronicle* dated 27th June 1889 quotes prices for Portland and Purbeck stone, rock faced and smooth faced, or lime, for delivery to all stations to Wareham and to Paddington. Limestone for shipping could be delivered to Weymouth Quay.

Prices per square yard by the truck load

	Rock faced	Smooth faced	Finest Portland lime per ton.
At the quarries	3s.0d.	4s.0d.	12s.0d.
Dorchester	5s.0d.	6s.0d.	14s.0d.
Wareham	5s.6d.	6s.6d.	15s.10d.
Paddington	8s.0d.	9s.0d.	10s.0d.

Isle of Portland

The fine quality freestones from the Isle of Portland were used initially by the Romans and there was occasional use during the Middle Ages, including examples where a bargeload of stone was taken to Exeter in 1303, and some to London in the 1340's. There are 35 named quarries on the Isle of Portland, of which Kingbarrow (SY691729) is now a nature reserve and Tout (SY685724) a sculpture park and

public open space. Bowers (SY654720), Perryfield (SY688712), Broadcroft (SY697718) and Withies Croft (SY694725) are still working. All have Portland and Purbeck formation present.

Quarries

SY677.685	Bill quarry
SY683.710	Grangecroft
SY684.688	Butts quarry
SY684.720	Bowers quarry
SY685.723	Trade quarries
SY685.724	Tout
SY686.711	Suckthumb
SY687.692	Longstone Ope
SY687.725	Wide Street
SY688.712	Perryfield
SY689.696	Breston
SY689.725	Inmosthay
SY690.697	God Nore
SY690.698	Sheat
SY690.699	Freshwater
SY691.729	Kingbarrow
SY692.703	Duncecroft
SY692.714	Cottonfields
SY694.711	Perryfield,
SY694.714	Bottom Coombe
SY694.721	Crown Farm
SY694.725	Withies Croft
SY694.726	Waycroft
SY695.721	Long Acre
SY695.725	Independent
SY696.706	Southwell, landslip
SY697.712	Wakeham East
SY697.717	Silklake
SY697.718	Broadcroft
SY697.724	Higher Headlands
SY697.729	Admiralty/Waycroft
SY698.715	Chalklands
SY700.718	Yeolands
SY702.717	Shephers Dinner

On the Isle of Portland itself most of the houses built up to the end of the nineteenth century are of Portland Stone, often using the Roach in square rather than rectangular blocks. At Church Ope Cove the remains of Rufus Castle, built in 1430, still cling precariously to the clifftop near Pennysylvania Castle, built for John Penn about 1800. The thirteenth century church of St. Andrew's was built of the Whit

Above Portland Castle was originally built for Henry VIII, but was improved during the Napoleonic wars.

Left St. George's church at Reforne on Portland was built by Thomas Gilbert, who selected the stone for Christopher Wren's churches in London. Here he used Roach, which is very hard and said to be difficult to work.

(1619-22). This building had stone from Oxfordshire for the upper part originally, but was refaced with Portland Stone by Sir John Soane in 1829.

In 1633 a new pier was built on Portland, with a new cartway to the quarry. However, in February 1696 a cliff fall destroyed the south pier. The north pier had been in disuse and could not be replaced because of shingle. Wren used the stone for many churches in London after the Great Fire (1666). The new St. Paul's Cathedral, started in 1675, was built of stone from the Grove Quarries and used over a million tons. Thomas Gilbert suggested a new wharf by Henry VIII's fort, but it proved too expensive. He designed the new church of St. George Reforne which was built of the Roach between 1754 and 1766. It was built to replace St. Andrew's church, on a cruciform plan. King George II subscribed £500 towards the building and further funds were raised by selling the pews. These pews were then willed to later family members. The elegant font was carved from the Best Bed by William Gilbert, Thomas's brother.

Nothe Fort was built of Roach to protect Weymouth from a Napoleonic invasion. The Verne was built originally as a barracks, but only the entrance gateway can be seen to be of Portland Stone. During the nineteenth century a prison was built on

Bed at Church Ope, but there is very little left of the building.

During Henry VIII's reign wars with France led to the building of many forts along the south coast of England. Portland Castle is at the north-eastern corner of Portland, to protect Portland Harbour. Hurst Castle stands on Hurst Spit at the narrow entrance to the Solent and is built of Portland Roach shipped there from Portland.

The introduction of frame-saws and water-power in the seventeenth century made it possible to cut larger blocks of stone. Inigo Jones who held the King's monopoly of Portland Stone used it for the lower courses of the Banqueting Hall in Whitehall

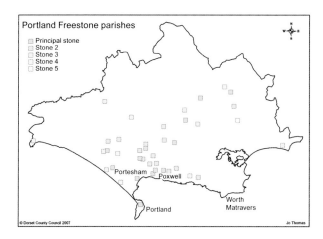

Kingston Maurward college was originally built of brick in the 18th century, but has been faced with Portland Freestone.

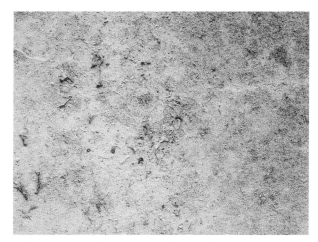

Whit Bed Portland Freestone in Shire Hall, Dorchester.

the highest point of the island and the convicts were employed to build the breakwaters and dockyard to create a sheltered harbour. The Admiralty remained on Portland until the end of the twentieth century.

In London the Goldsmiths Hall and the Reform Club were built of the top (Whit) bed from Waycroft Quarry (SY694726). Greenwich Hospital, the British Museum (1753) and Somerset House (1776) were built of the Whit Bed. The new addition in the courtyard of the British Museum should have been Whit Bed from the Isle of Portland, but it is in fact from France. The texture of the stone is a fair match for the Whit Bed, but the colour is far too yellow. Portland's whiteness is its most recognisable characteristic.

In Dorchester the old Shire Hall was designed by Thomas Hardwick and built in High West Street in 1795-7 of Portland ashlar. What is now the Agricultural College at Kingston Maurward was originally built in brick for George Pitt in the early

eighteenth century, but was cased in Portland stone in 1794. It is said that when the king came to visit he was not complimentary about the brick, and so the current owner had it cased in stone.

Increasing use of Portland Stone took place during the eighteenth, nineteenth and twentieth centuries, not only in London but also in Dublin, Cardiff, Leeds, Southampton and Manchester. The new War Office building in London was built in 1901 from Wakeham quarry (SY697712).

Most of the Portland Stone in Dublin is used for steps, cills, columns and dressings, including the Museum built in 1857. There is plenty of good building stone in Ireland, which was used for most of the buildings. However the Parliament building, now used as the Bank of Ireland, was faced with Portland Stone in 1729-31, and City Hall, designed by Thomas Coolly in 1769 was also faced with Portland Stone. The Rotunda in Parnell Street was built in 1757. In 1911 the Government Offices, built for the Royal College of Science and designed by Sir Aston Webb and Sir Thomas Manley Deane were the last conventional buildings faced with Portland Stone. Clery's in Connell Street was built on a steel frame with stone facing soon after 1916.

When coastal shipping improved in the early eighteenth century, Portland Stone was taken round the coast and up the river to Cambridge, where there was little durable stone to build the colleges. In King's College the Gibbs Building (1724-59) was the first use of Portland in Cambridge. The east range

Above This stone of Portland Freestone marking the Mason-Dixon line is at the south-west corner of the state of Delaware on its common border with Maryland, U.S.A. (© Pete Zapadka/exploretheline.com).

Below Quarried galleries east of Winspit, Worth Matravers, in the Under Freestone of the Portland Freestone. The stone was lifted into boats from the cliffs when the weather was calm.

of the Schools Building (1754-8) and the Senate House (1722-30) are both faced with Portland. The Fitzwilliam Museum, built between 1837 and 1849, whose first architect George Basevi was killed by a fall at Ely Cathedral in 1845, was completed by the second Charles Robert Cockerell, in Portland stone. The colourful interior of the entrance hall, designed by Edward M. Barry, cost over £23,000. The modern buildings straddling King's Lane are faced with Portland Roach, and the new Howard building in Downing College has columns of white Portland Stone that contrast strongly with the yellow Ketton oolite.

In Cardiff land was bought from the Marquess of Bute at the end of the nineteenth century in order to build a new civic centre. The complex of buildings including City Hall and the Museum were built of Portland Stone in the 1920's. Another steel framed building faced with Portland Stone is the Council House in Nottingham (1929) designed by T.C. Howitt. Several other buildings in Old Market Square are also faced with Portland.

The Portland Freestone has also been exported overseas, including America where it was used for colonial buildings in Virginia during the eighteenth century and for marking the Mason-Dixon line. This line was surveyed between 1763 and 1767 by Charles Mason and Jeremiah Dixon to resolve a dispute between the colonies of Maryland and Pennsylvania, Delaware and West Virginia. The line is marked by stones every mile and 'crownstones' every five miles

that have the coat of arms of Maryland's founding Calvert family on one side and on the other side the arms of William Penn. During the 1920's the Freestone was exported to Sydney and New Delhi for their civic buildings.

The Cenotaph was designed by Edwin Lutyens in 1919 of Portland Freestone. The same stone and often the same design have been used for war memorials all over England. War graves in Europe and in the United Kingdom are marked by headstones of Portland Freestone that are systematically renewed, the Portland quarries taking it in turn to provide them. Portland Freestone is also used over a wide area of Dorset for ordinary graves

ISLE OF PURBECK

In the Isle of Purbeck the cliff quarries provided Portland stone that was used in Norman work in Christchurch Priory and in the fifteenth century west tower. These quarries may have been used earlier than those on Portland because they were easier to reach. Galleries were cut horizontally into the cliffs and the stone loaded into ships that came close in when the weather was calm. Carvings of some of these ships can be seen on the walls of Winspit quarry (SY977761). The quarries have been excavated into the cliffs from St. Aldhelm's Head to Durlston Head, and at Winspit and Seacombe have taken advantage of the coombes cut by streams leading to the coast.

The main quarries are:

SY963753	Portland Freestone	St. Aldhelm's Head
SY964762	Portland Freestone	St. Aldhelm's quarry
SY968783	Portland Freestone & Cherty Beds	Swanworth (roadstone only)
SY977761	Portland Freestone	Winspit.
SY984766	Portland Freestone	Seacombe
SY997769	Portland Freestone	Dancing Ledge
SY031769	Portland Freestone	Tilly Whim.

Several manor houses in Dorset built before the seventeenth century are recorded as using Purbeck stone, but on examination are seen to be of Portland Freestone from the Isle of Purbeck. The stone is often referred to as 'Purbeck-Portland'.

Kingston Russell house was built of Portland Freestone possibly from the Isle of Purbeck in the mid seventeenth and early eighteenth century. The earlier part faces east, and is of a different style from the eighteenth century Palladian west front built

The main front of Smedmore House, Kimmeridge, is built of Portland Freestone from the cliff quarries.

for John Michel before 1739. Other manor houses thought to be of 'Purbeck-Portland' are Herringston (originally sixteenth century), the old manor house at Kingston Maurward (sixteenth century), Lulworth Castle (1608), Tyneham (now a ruin), and Creech Grange (eighteenth century). In later buildings it was used for door and window surrounds, and for quoins in vernacular buildings whose walls were mostly of Purbeck stone. Although a source in the Isle of Purbeck seems perfectly sensible for Lulworth, Tyneham and Creech Grange, Kingston Maurward, Herringston and Kingston Russell could just as easily have been built of stone from the Ridgeway.

A weathered block of Portland Freestone in the tower of Wimborne Minster seems to match the Under Freestone in Winspit Quarry, Worth Matravers. The large pieces of broken shell are surrounded by ooliths (as seen through a handlens).

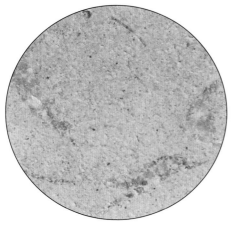

Above St. Aldhelm's Quarry in 2002. Both Portland and Purbeck limestones are stored and worked on this site.

Left A cut piece of Portland Freestone Spangle from St. Aldhelm's Quarry in Worth Matravers. The shells have been replaced by crystals of calcite that shine when fresh-cut. This stone is now used for interior cladding of walls in prestigious buildings (as seen through a handlens).

The stone from Purbeck was said to be harder and denser than that from Portland, particularly Tilly Whim, and was used for landings and steps that would have to take hard wear. The caves at Tilly Whim were still in use up to 1811, and were a tourist attraction until the 1950's, but have now partly collapsed. At Seacombe the Headbury and Cliff Field quarries are on the east, and the Halsewell on the west, working underground. Howe (1910) records that the Under Freestone from Winspit was used for kerbs, gutters and sinks. The House Cap (above the Under Freestone) is coarse-grained, and was used for breakwaters. The *Titanites* (Blue) Bed was used for lintels and gate-posts. He also records that it was used to build the lighthouse in Margate, the prison at Winchester, Clock House in Dover, the West India Docks in London, and many churches. Encombe House was built of stone in 1735 for John Pitt from London Doors quarry (SY945793), on the rim of the Golden Bowl, to the north of the house.

Stone from St. Aldhelm's quarry is still being worked. The Spangle is in great demand for interior cladding where the sparkle of the calcite crystals is not dimmed by weathering.

VALE OF WARDOUR

Stone quarried from Chilmark and Tisbury is used in east and north Dorset. It is the same age as the Portland Formations, but the area had a different environment at the time of deposition. The Upper Building Stones are a fine-grained white or buff sandy oolitic limestone (equivalent to the *Titanites* Bed of the Portland Limestone Formation at St. Aldhelm's) and has been used for the carved west front at Salisbury Cathedral.

The Main Building Stones are glauconitic sandy limestones varying from green to buff in colour. They are part of the lower Portland Sand Formation. In colour this glauconitic sandstone (Tisbury Sandstone) is very similar to Upper Greensand, but while both sandstones have a calcite cement, the Tisbury is finer grained and withstands weathering more effectively. It has been used for bridges and sluice gates in the Tarrant and Stour valleys as well as house building.

The thirteenth century hunting lodge which is now Cranborne Manor has rendered rubble walls, but the ashlar dressings and seventeenth century work on the northern side of the house are of Tisbury Sandstone. At Iwerne Minster, the main house at Clayesmore School is built of white stone from Tisbury, with Ham Hill Stone dressings.

Purbeck Limestones

GEOLOGY

The Purbeck Formation is a series of limestones, shales and calcareous clays that formed in shallow fresh or brackish water lagoons in a warm climate. About half way through the Formation is a thick bed of oysters indicating that sea levels rose temporarily to increase the salinity of the water. The Formation is now considered to be at the beginning of the Cretaceous, approximately 140 to 145 million years old. At this time Dorset was still south of its present position on the globe, about at the latitude of today's Mediterranean and the climate was comparable to that of the Red Sea, or parts of southern Australia.

Recent work by geologists has divided the Purbeck Limestone Group into two Formations, the lower Lulworth Formation and the upper Durlston Formation from the base of the oyster bed (Cinder Bed) upwards. These Formations have been divided into Members with a particular reference section, and the Members into beds with names familiar to geologists over many years. However the old divisions of Lower, Middle and Upper Purbeck are still in common use.

At the beginning of Purbeck times algal limestones forming on top of the marine dunes of the Portland limestone were followed by a soil horizon on two occasions. *Cupressus* type trees that grew in those soils have been found fossilised within the succeeding algal limestones. The sea must have been retreating.

Above this fossil forest horizon are laminated fine micrite limestones in the Mupe Member (Lulworth Formation). In the western area of Portland and the Ridgeway the laminated limestones, although containing some evaporites, have remained intact. In the eastern area of the Isle of Purbeck, however, the evaporites may have been originally more extensive and later have dissolved, leading to collapse of the beds. These collapsed beds are known as the Broken Beds. Within the Broken Beds some small pieces show the crystal shapes of the evaporite halite (salt)

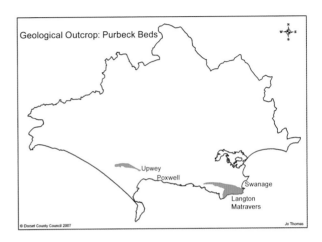

– known as 'halite pseudomorphs'.

The laminated limestones above the Broken Beds are known as the Cypris Freestones, since they contain many fossils of *Cypris* – ostracods, a type of crustacea that lived in brackish environments. Ostracods of later species can still be found living in brackish conditions today. These Freestones are used for building in the area north of Weymouth and Dorchester as far east as Coombe Keynes near Wool and as far west as Abbotsbury. These thick beds of ostracod-rich limestones are followed by dark mudstones of the Ridgeway Member (Lulworth Formation).

The environment changed to freshwater lagoons in a warm environment but with the sea further away, so that the formation of evaporites lessened. There are considerable thicknesses of dark, organic rich shales that formed from mud lacking in oxygen. These shales alternate with thin limestones containing bivalves and gastropods. The remains of insects are found in the shales, and the names of the beds often reflect the fossils that have been found – Insect Beds, or Soft Cockle Beds for instance. Large gypsum masses occur in the shales, with limestone beds draped around them. This gypsum was quarried in Durlston Bay and used for plaster of Paris. Towards

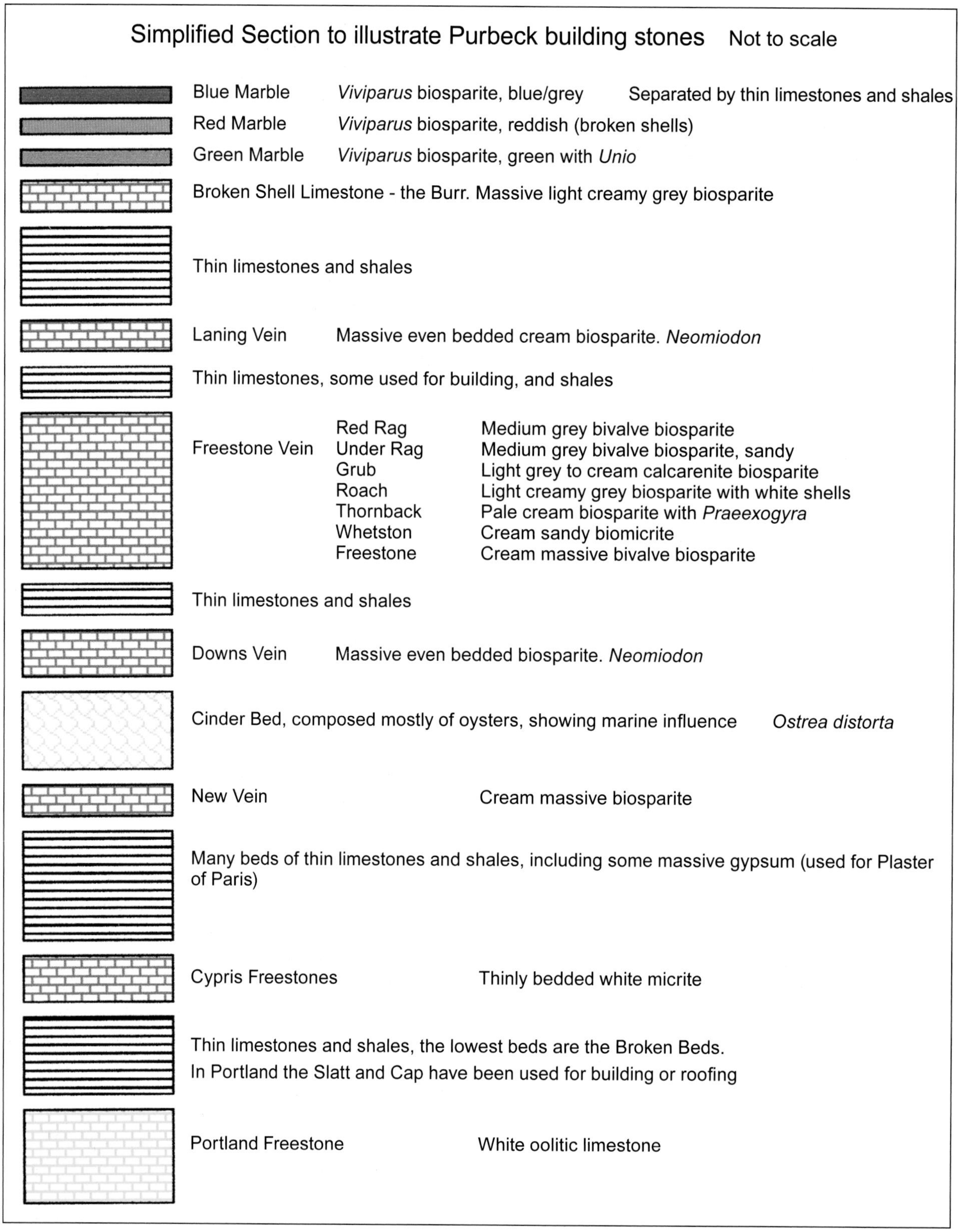

Simplified Section to illustrate Purbeck building stones   Not to scale

Blue Marble — *Viviparus* biosparite, blue/grey   Separated by thin limestones and shales

Red Marble — *Viviparus* biosparite, reddish (broken shells)

Green Marble — *Viviparus* biosparite, green with *Unio*

Broken Shell Limestone - the Burr. Massive light creamy grey biosparite

Thin limestones and shales

Laning Vein — Massive even bedded cream biosparite. *Neomiodon*

Thin limestones, some used for building, and shales

Freestone Vein		
	Red Rag	Medium grey bivalve biosparite
	Under Rag	Medium grey bivalve biosparite, sandy
	Grub	Light grey to cream calcarenite biosparite
	Roach	Light creamy grey biosparite with white shells
	Thornback	Pale cream biosparite with *Praeexogyra*
	Whetston	Cream sandy biomicrite
	Freestone	Cream massive bivalve biosparite

Thin limestones and shales

Downs Vein — Massive even bedded biosparite. *Neomiodon*

Cinder Bed, composed mostly of oysters, showing marine influence   *Ostrea distorta*

New Vein — Cream massive biosparite

Many beds of thin limestones and shales, including some massive gypsum (used for Plaster of Paris)

Cypris Freestones — Thinly bedded white micrite

Thin limestones and shales, the lowest beds are the Broken Beds.
In Portland the Slatt and Cap have been used for building or roofing

Portland Freestone — White oolitic limestone

the end of the Soft Cockle beds the shales decrease and there are many different beds of limestone, often containing gypsum crystals. All these beds were previously known as the Lower Purbeck.

The Middle Purbeck starts with the Marly Freshwater Beds, and Cherty Freshwater Beds limestones and clays that contain gastropods and have been burrowed, possibly by crustaceans. The first of the thick limestones quarried for building is the New Vein. The New Vein (in the Cherty Freshwater Beds) is a massive rough-bedded limestone containing fossils of the gastropods *Hydrobia* and *Viviparus*. The Cap Bed above, a thinner bed, contains the gastropods *Viviparus* and *Valvata*. The Feather bed has several different bivalves. The Button Bed is an ostracod rich limestone with chert. These beds are now in the Worbarrow Tout Member of the Lulworth Formation.

Three thick beds of oysters, known as the Cinder Bed, show an incursion of the sea into the lagoonal area. The base of this bed is the end of the Lulworth Formation. Above it is the Durlston Formation. At one time the base of the Cretaceous was taken to be at the base of the Cinder Bed, but more recent research has put the base of the Cretaceous at the base of the entire Purbeck sequence.

The majority of quarries in the Isle of Purbeck are in the Middle Purbeck beds, now named the Stair Hole Member of the Durlston Formation, where groups of useful beds are referred to by the quarrymen as Veins. Most of the Veins of building stone are above the Cinder Bed. The Downs Vein is a massive cream limestone that splits easily, with some chert at the top. The bivalves are mostly white. It is separated from the Cinder Bed by some muddy limestones and shales and is followed by the Laper and Lias Rag and the various beds that make up the Freestone Vein. This Vein consists of several different limestones with very little intervening shales. The different beds are all used for building and many of them contain bivalve fossils. The greyish beds have grey mussel or oyster shells, and other bivalves, while the cream coloured beds are packed with small *Neomiodon*. They are, in ascending order;

• the Blue Bed, a shell fragment sparite limestone with mixed bivalves;
• the Freestone, entirely *Neomiodon* and very similar to Burr, the bivalves being replaced by sparite and in random orientation;

• the Whetston, a sandy limestone with grey and white shells replaced by sparite;
• Thornback, a sparite limestone with micrite supporting the shell fragments that are mostly white, but with some grey small oysters;
• Grey Bed, with mixed bivalves;
• Roach has recognisable *Neomiodon and Viviparus*, a sparite limestone with micrite filling the pore spaces;
• Grub, a sandy limestone with a greater proportion of grey shells;
• Under Rag and the Red Rag are both rough, massive sandy limestones with *Neomiodon,* the Under Rag containing *Viviparus*.

At the top of many of the quarries in the Middle Purbeck, the Laning Vein is also a cream coloured sandy limestone in which the shells have been replaced by sparite. Fine-grained micrite cement supports the shell fragments, but pore spaces can be seen inside the empty shells. The consistently recognisable beds across the Isle of Purbeck, with their particular assemblies of fossils, indicate restricted environments where at times only a few species of bivalves could survive. The alternation of limestones and shales continues, but few beds are of use for building.

The Peveril Point Member of the Durlston Formation is placed at the base of the massive Broken Shell Limestone. Known to quarrymen as the Burr, in the Upper Purbeck Beds, this appears in the cliff at Peveril Point, Swanage and continues inland along the lower slope of the valley to Worbarrow Bay. The shells are exclusively *Neomiodon*. The broken shell material, in random orientation, has been replaced by sparite with scattered pieces of dark shells. The pieces of shell support each other, leaving open pore spaces. This gives the stone good porosity, so that it will dry out quickly.

Above the Burr are shales, with the Green Marble containing *Viviparus* and *Unio* fossils, the Red Marble containing *Viviparus* and smaller bivalves, and the Blue Marble containing only *Viviparus*. The carbonate cement in the Marbles appears to be more crystalline than most of the other limestones, with no empty pore spaces. The Purbeck Marbles are limestones with a crystalline cement that can be polished, not true marbles where heat and pressure have changed the whole rock into interlocking crystals.

LANDSCAPE

The three areas of outcrop of the Purbeck limestones are on the northern and southern limbs of the Weymouth anticline, and the southern half of the Isle of Purbeck. On the northern edge of the Weymouth anticline the Purbeck limestones overlie the Portland limestones, capping hills south of the Chalk Ridgeway from Portesham eastwards. Both Formations dip steeply north, and present a steep scarp face to the south. East of Weymouth the hills and outcrop are broken by faulting and folding that occurred before the deposition of the Cretaceous Upper Greensand. At Poxwell a pericline clea rly shows as a boat shape on the hills either side of the main road. The southern edge of the Weymouth anticline is exposed on the Isle of Portland, where the lowest Purbeck limestones cap most of the island.

In the Isle of Purbeck the sea cliffs are of Portland limestone, with only a small capping of the lowest Purbeck beds, the steep scarp face of the remainder having been weathered back northwards. The faults and folding within the Purbeck beds can only be seen in the open quarries. Overall, they are dipping northwards, with a gradual slope from the seaward scarp down to Langton and Worth Matravers, and a steeper slope from there down to the valley at Wilkswood. The upper Purbeck beds, including the Burr and Marbles, have been weathered away from the upper slopes, and are only preserved on the lower slopes of the valley. At Peveril Point the Marbles form two reefs on either side of a tight fold. At the northern end of Worbarrow Tout the Marbles are mostly covered by shingle.

QUARRYING AND USE IN BUILDINGS

Limestones from the Purbeck Beds have been used locally from Roman times to the present day, and have also been exported by sea from the Norman Conquest until the nineteenth century. They have therefore been recorded by historians as building stones and by geologists during both the nineteenth and twentieth centuries. Not all the descriptions published by geologists agree with each other on the divisions named, but this is understandable when faced with thin beds of limestone where the characters are similar, and the divisions debatable. The quarrymen and masons are more likely to

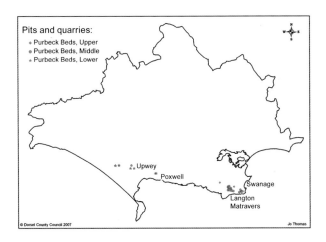

agree with each other. Hutchins, Pevsner, the Royal Commission on Historical Monuments and the Victoria County History record the stone from the historical point of view, and Bristow, Austen, Arkell, Clements, Ensom and others have recorded the sequence from the geologists' point of view. Detailed works on the geology are in Further Reading.

In the latter half of the nineteenth century several geologists published measured sections in the quarries 'near Swanage', but the exact position of their measurements was not recorded. It is therefore difficult to correlate their sections -- almost certainly measured in different places. During the twentieth century geologists have been more careful to locate their measurements, but it is still a subjective science, and difficult to correlate the beds seen in the different quarries or cliff sections. The quarrymen, whose families have worked the stone for centuries, can recognise the same bed of stone in different places. However, they will point out that the precise character of the bed, in texture, fossil content and suitability for building, changes rapidly. Since in this book we are concerned with building stone it is preferable to use the quarrymen's names for the beds.

On the Isle of Portland the algal limestones, named the Cap, have been used for building in the Bow and Arrow castle. Above the Cap the oldest beds used for building, the laminated micrites, are known as the Cypris Freestones, the *Cypris* being an ostracod or microscopic crustacean. These were quarried from the hills south of the Ridgeway between Weymouth and Dorchester. From Portesham (SY609860) to Poxwell (SY743835) the quarries produced both Portland Freestone and the Purbeck limestones from quarries cut into the side of the hills, and the Cypris

Freestones were also mined underground from Green Hill near Chalbury (SY694842). The stone from all these quarries is known to historians as Ridgeway stone, but when individual quarries are named, it could be referring to either Portland or Purbeck limestone.

Vernacular buildings and small churches from Portesham to Poxwell are built of the Purbeck limestones from the Ridgeway quarries. Although the Cypris Freestones appear smooth in situ, the characteristic weathering suggests a regular change in sedimentation so that thin algal layers weather out more easily. The use of Lower Purbeck Ridgeway stone from Portesham has already been mentioned in Litton Cheney church. The Middle and Upper Purbeck limestones are also present in the buildings to a lesser degree. An excavation for a water supply at Friar Waddon uncovered the Broken Shell Limestone (Upper Purbeck Burr) and the recent re-survey by the British Geological Survey shows that the whole sequence is present at Upwey (SY670851) and Poxwell. The altar slab in Corton Chapel, and the Saxon carving of an angel in Winterborne Steepleton church certainly appear to be of a limestone made up of *Neomiodon* shells. The *Neomiodon* shells are present in all the Middle Purbeck limestone beds and in the Upper Purbeck Burr.

The Purbeck limestones, including the laminated micrite characteristic of the Ridgeway quarries are also used in Weymouth and Dorchester. Excavations at Maiden Castle have found the footings of Iron Age buildings using stone from Upwey. It seems possible that the Roman road that ran south from Dorchester went through the quarries near the hamlet of Ridgeway in Upwey. The Roman town

Above left In Litton Cheney church tower the dripstone is Ham Hill Stone, and the white laminated stone is Lower Purbeck Cypris Freestone.

Above Colliton House, near County Hall, Dorchester, is built of Lower Purbeck Cypris Freestone from the Ridgeway quarries that stretched from Portesham to Upwey and Chalbury to Poxwell.

Below The Roman wall at Top o' Town, Dorchester is built of the Lower Purbeck Cypris Freestone from Upwey Quarry.

house and remnant of town wall were built of stone from Upwey, mixed with flint. Windsbatch quarry (SY658851) near Upwey church provided stone for the Tower of London in the reign of Edward III. The local stone was used for the buildings in Upwey, including the mill, but Hutchins (II, p 840) records that the stone was also used flat for flagstones and on edge for boundary walls. The spire of All Saints church in Dorchester was built of the Cypris Freestones, in 1843-5, designed by Benjamin Ferrey.

Woodsford Castle in the Frome valley was built

Above Woodsford Castle was built of Lower Purbeck Cypris Freestone from the eastern Ridgeway quarries.

Below In the 15th century Hospice in Cerne Abbas the Lower Purbeck Cypris Freestone is banded with flint. The oriel window includes Portland limestone and the orange blocks are Ham Hill Stone. The interior walls of the Hospice are lined with Chalk block.

of Upwey stone in the fourteenth century. The Ridgeway stone was also used in the villages of the Frome valley, and its tributaries, the Piddle, Cerne and south Winterborne.

It has been used in the upper Piddle valley, most noticeably in the churches, which have walls of dressed Purbeck limestones and quoins, window mullions and doorways of the Portland Freestone ashlar. The *Dorset County Chronicle* records that in February 1868 the church in Piddlehinton was being restored with flint and Ridgeway stone. Red Poole tiles were placed on the floor of the nave and aisle. In the lower Piddle valley, Puddletown church and Athelhampton have been built of stone from

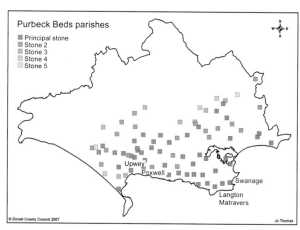

the Ridgeway. Coombe Keynes church, south of Wool was rebuilt in the nineteenth century, using some stone from the old building, and is a mixture of Purbeck stone from the Ridgeway quarries and the local ironstone. Records state that the previous church had a good deal of flint in its construction.

In the Cerne valley the Cypris Freestones have been used in Cerne Abbas, as will be described in the chapter on the use of Chalk, and in Nether Cerne the farmhouse and church have a mixture of Cypris Freestones and flint.

The church in Winterborne Abbas has bands of Cypris Freestones and flint in the chancel, with the nave and tower of various Purbeck limestones. At Winterbourne Steepleton the tower is built of Portland and Lower Purbeck limestones and flint. It is thought that the nave, of Lower Purbeck and flint, is late Anglo-Saxon.

Most of the vernacular buildings in the Isle of Purbeck use the Middle Purbeck building stones from quarries in Worth Matravers, Langton Matravers and Swanage. The earliest excavations were open surface pits known as riddings. This was followed by driving shafts into the scarp face of the hills above the cliffs, and later into the upper north-facing slopes between Swanage and Langton Matravers. The beds of useful limestone were so thin that these mines were often only 3 feet (less than 1 metre) high and the men therefore had to work crouched down. When the Freestone Vein was being worked, the Grub was left as the roof of the mine, the Roach, Thornback, Whetston and Freestone being taken away. This was the thickest Vein, so that when the Laning Vein, Downs Vein or New Vein were worked the men had to remove the shale beds above and below in order to have room to work. Within the mine the stone could be moved on wheeled trolleys that were then drawn up an inclined shaft on rails. The winch, which was turned by a donkey, and the rails can still be seen in a restored quarry entrance in Langton Matravers.

After the Second World War machines became available that could strip the topsoil from the fields, allowing the quarrymen to dig the stone more easily. In the 1960's hydraulic machines that could also lift the stone were introduced. Since then quarrying has been opencast in deep excavations. The depth of the individual quarries now depends on which Vein the quarryman is seeking. Usually the Downs Vein is the deepest, as the Cinder Bed is so hard to break through in order to reach the New Vein. In many

Above Norman's Quarry, Langton Matravers.

Below Lovell's Quarry, Acton, in 1997.

open quarries it is now possible to see a full sequence from the Laning Vein down to the Downs Vein.

The Freestone is the best quality for building in the Middle Purbeck, being in thick beds that can be cut as ashlar. The manor house at Dunshay was one of the earliest to be built of Freestone in 1642. The Freestone was used a good deal during the nineteenth century for churches in Poole and Bournemouth as these towns expanded rapidly. The dressings of these churches are often of Bath Stone that came by rail after 1860. Langton Matravers church is mostly Freestone, and includes some decorative work using the Cherty Freshwater Beds.

The Middle Purbeck limestones have also been used for paving and kerbstones in Poole, Christchurch, Wimborne and London. The trade in paving stones was mostly in the nineteenth century, when thousands of tons were shipped from Swanage to London. The Downs Vein can be split into slabs 8 – 10 centimetres thick and has been used mainly for

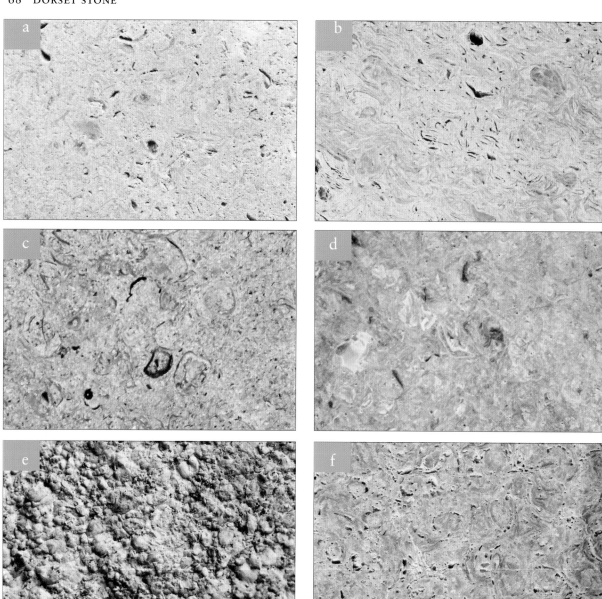

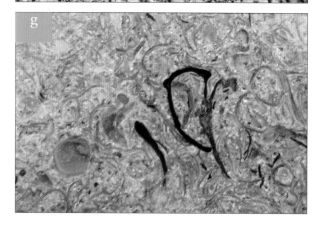

Samples of limestones from the Middle Purbeck quarried recently in the Isle of Purbeck.

a) Freestone from Swanage. Although recognisably the same stone, the quarrymen will emphasise the difference.

b) Freestone from Acton.

c) Thornback. Note the darker oyster shells and the lack of cavities in the stone.

d) Wetston

e) Roach - a weathered surface showing gastropods and bivalves.

f) Downs Vein – a more open textured limestone, packed with cream coloured Neomiodon.

g) Grub – light coloured 'Corbula' and dark *Praeexogyra* .

paving. The small pieces left when larger slabs were exported have been used to build the cottages near to the quarries in Acton, Worth Matravers and Langton Matravers.

The Roach, Thornback and Grub from the Freestone Vein have also been used for paving, for steps, setts and kerbs. Flat paving was used in the eighteenth and nineteenth centuries, but rwoadways which had to take greater wear from horses hooves and the wheels of carts were paved with setts. These were brick-shaped cut pieces of stone turned on edge, so that the wear was taken across the grain of the stone and there was less danger of the road becoming slippery. The Grub and Thornback containing grey

St. James' church in Poole was built of Middle Purbeck Freestone ashlar. Many churches in Poole and Bournemouth were built of Middle Purbeck limestone during the nineteenth century, but most were rock-faced.

Above Cottages in Worth Matravers built of local Purbeck limestone.

Below Quarrymen's cottages in Acton are built and roofed with local Middle Purbeck limestone.

shells seem to predominate in those examples that survive today. Kerbstones are similarly used edge on to the pavements.

Thinner slabs of the Downs Vein up to 2 centimetres thick have been used as roofing tiles throughout the Isle of Purbeck and up the Frome valley. It splits easily and is firm enough to knock a peg hole into. It was originally taken from shallow outcrops on the side of the hill, rather than quarried in the underground shafts. In the fifteenth century roofing stone was exported from Poole. In the reign of Edward IV a foreign ship, either Dutch or Flemish, took 30,000 stones valued at £4. They were referred

Above A closer view of a roof in Worth Matravers. The roof tiles are laid in diminishing courses towards the apex.

Left North Street in Langton Matravers.

to as 'sclatte stones', a term also used in the Isle of Portland for thin-bedded stones suitable for roofing.

The roofing tiles were often a by-product of the paving works. The weight of the Purbeck roofing tiles has been quoted at 1.25 tons to every 100 sq. ft. (A. Clifton-Taylor 1987). This meant that the joists supporting the roof needed to be strong enough to hold such a weight. In many cases only two or three courses of stone tiles are now laid where the eaves can support the weight, while the remainder of the roof is covered with slates or clay tiles. They were at one time laid on a bed of moss, but later have been bedded in hair and lime mortar. Occasionally slabs from the Roach, Thornback, Grub or New Vein have been thin enough for use as roofing tiles. The size of these tiles, particularly when seen from inside a roof, is considerably larger than the stone tiles used in West Dorset. They are not cut to size, but simply sorted so that the smallest are at the apex of the roof,

the largest near the eaves. They may be as much as 90 centimetres long and 60 centimetres wide.

Most of the beds of limestone are thin and the blocks used in the cottages are not much larger than a clay brick. The stone is built as coursed dressed rubble, with larger blocks as quoins. Windows and doorways are often of the Portland limestone quarried from the cliffs. The Whetston and Thornback can both be used out of bed and therefore have been used as headstones for graves, and the Thornback for quoins and window frames. Ramsgate harbour walls were constructed of Purbeck stone in 1750-52.

In the remainder of Dorset many historic buildings in Poole, Christchurch and Wimborne are of Purbeck stone. In Poole, Scaplen's Court and the Maritime Museum (originally the town cellars) were built of dressed Purbeck limestone. The thirteenth century north porch of Christchurch Priory was built of Purbeck Burr limestone but the fifteenth century west tower is of Portland Freestone from the Isle of Purbeck known as Cliff Stone, or Purbeck-Portland. The villages of the Stour valley could be reached by boat through Christchurch and the medieval churches of Holdenhurst, Kinson, Canford Magna and Wimborne Minster all used Purbeck stone with a mix of local heathstone. The stone bridges over the Stour, built and repeatedly widened or repaired over many centuries, also contain Purbeck stone and occasionally the local heathstone.

In the Isle of Purbeck the older buildings, such as Corfe Castle, Worth Matravers and Studland

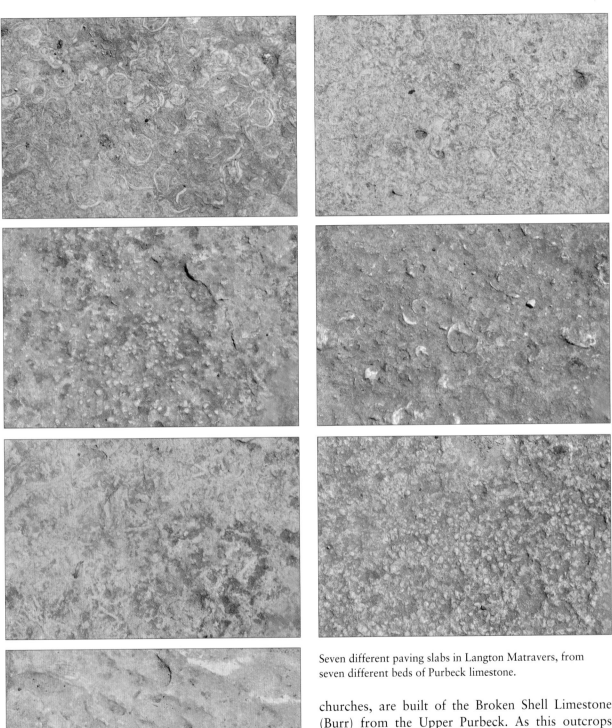

Seven different paving slabs in Langton Matravers, from seven different beds of Purbeck limestone.

churches, are built of the Broken Shell Limestone (Burr) from the Upper Purbeck. As this outcrops on the lower slope of the hill south of Corfe Castle it would have been the easiest to reach, as well as being in massive beds that could be cut as ashlar. The Burr can be found in medieval ecclesiastical buildings within Dorset, at Milton Abbey in the old east wall and Crawford Abbey in the remains of the barn, as well as Christchurch Priory. In the

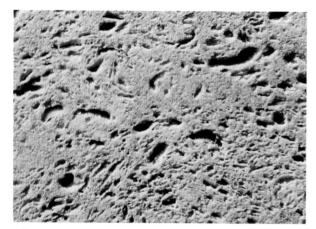

Above A cut sample of the Burr, or Broken Shell Limestone from the Upper Purbeck. Found in thick beds that outcrop on the north-facing slope of the valley between Swanage and Corfe Castle, this was the most important building stone used by the Normans and into medieval times.

Below A broken piece of the Burr, from Crack Lane Quarry, Langton Matravers.

Below In the North Tower of Corfe Castle, built by King John, both the white Purbeck limestone and the rusty-coloured Marble have been used. The Marble contains more iron than the other beds and therefore 'rusts' when exposed to the weather.

Above A cut sample of the blue Purbeck Marble. The whorls are all *Viviparus* gastropods cut through at random angles. The blue Purbeck Marble consists of *Viviparus* gastropods with dark shells filled with calcite crystals surrounded by cream micrite. The limestone will take a polish and when used inside buildings will stay fresh for many centuries. However, the small iron content in the cement will oxidise if exposed to damp and the stone will crumble [as seen through a handlens].

thirteenth century it was also taken, presumably by sea and up the river, to Winchester Castle. Henry VIII's fortifications at Brownsea Island were built of Purbeck Burr limestone. In older buildings centuries of weathering have brought out the difference from the Downs Vein and the Freestone, for though all three are cream coloured, the shells in the Burr are broken and tumbled in every direction, while the limestone matrix has weathered away into cavernous holes. The original Norman bridge south of Wareham was built of Burr, as was St. Martin's, the late Saxon church on the walls to the north of the town.

The last quarry in the Burr was near Crack Lane in Langton Matravers, and was opened to provide stone for the bridges over the Swanage Railway in the nineteenth century. It has also proved a beautiful sculptural stone. The beds of stone can still be seen in this Regionally Important Geological Site. (SY998792).

The Green, Red and Blue Purbeck Marbles are not true marbles, being shelly limestones that can take a polish because they have crystalline calcite as a cement between the gastropod fossils. Owing to the iron content in the limestone, if used outside the polish soon weathers away and the stone turns a pale rusty colour.

The Romans used Purbeck Marble at Silchester and Verulamium (ST. Albans), and the Saxons for fonts and grave-slabs. Purbeck Marble has been so highly prized for interior church columns and monuments that it can be found all over England. King John (1199-1216) is said to have been the first to appreciate its qualities and to exploit it. As a building stone it has been used in some of the farmhouses on the outcrop along the valley from Crack Lane through Quarr and Dunshay to Lynch, as would be expected, but rarely elsewhere because the iron in the stone tends to oxidise and the stone crumbles. However in that part of Corfe Castle built by King John there are a few pieces of the edge of one of the Marble beds, where micritic limestone is part of the bed. The farmhouses on the Purbeck Marble outcrop are referred to as manors, not because they are parish manor houses but because they were originally the centre of Marble quarrying for their particular area.

In Christchurch, the Constable's house (1160) and the Keep include large amounts of the Marble with other Purbeck and local stones. Although weathered, the Marble pieces have thus lasted over 800 years. Almost certainly they would have been rendered over during most of their life. This early use may have been sourced from pebbles on the beach at Peveril Point, rather than specifically quarried. The blue marble is the most commonly used in the slender columns in medieval churches, as well as the grave slabs of bishops or locally important persons. It is easily recognised by the sections cut through the fossil gastropod *Viviparus*. The red and green marbles also contain *Viviparus*, though more scattered, with the addition of *Unio* in the green. These are coloured by glauconite and other minerals. Across Dorset many fonts and graveslabs are of Purbeck Marble. At Whitchurch Canonicorum, the slab on top of St. Wite's tomb is of the blue marble and a floor graveslab of the green marble.

As a structural material, for columns and capitals the earliest example may be in Wolvesey Palace at Winchester (c. 1141). Many churches built between

Top The Constable's House in Christchurch was built during the 12th century of Purbeck limestone, brought by sea. There is a surprisingly large amount of Purbeck Marble in the construction.

Bottom Purbeck Marble effigy of a priest in the church porch in Abbotsbury. The damp atmosphere has oxidised the surface iron to change the colour of the stone to a light brown.

The effigy of a knight in Horton church is of Purbeck Marble, but his lady's effigy is of Ham Hill Stone.

1170 and 1350 have columns, carvings, fonts and effigies. In Puddletown church a canopied Martyn tomb is of Purbeck Marble. The nave columns in Salisbury Cathedral (1258) were built of the blue marble during Bishop Poore's time. His tomb, with a Purbeck Marble graveslab, is in Tarrant Crawford church, accompanied by the tomb of a Queen of Scotland whose slab is recorded as costing 100 shillings. The stone for the pillars in Salisbury Cathedral was given from a quarry near Downshay Manor that provided eight feet long blocks of stone.

The earliest use of the Marble in a Cathedral is in the piers of the Galilee Chapel of Durham Cathedral (1170-76) during the bishopric of Bishop Hugh Pudsey. Purbeck Marble and stone were exported to London for Westminster Abbey in 1257, and the stone was also used for the King's Palace at Westminster. The Marble is used for the facing material of the piers in Westminster Abbey and Exeter Cathedral in the fourteenth century. In Horton church an early fourteenth century effigy of a knight in Purbeck Marble lies next to his lady carved in Ham Hill Stone.

Before the port of Swanage was developed, stone from Purbeck was carted across the heathland from Corfe Castle to Ower Quay and taken in flat-bottomed boats to the deeper water quays at Poole for export around the coast. By the eighteenth century the stone from the Worth and Langton Matravers quarries was brought down into Swanage by cart and deposited on the shore or banks built above highwater. It was then carried in high-wheeled carts into the sea, transferred into boats, and then to larger vessels.

Open cast quarrying in Worth and Langton Matravers is now providing Middle Purbeck limestone for new building and repairs across Dorset. Where the original buildings are of Purbeck limestone, this is consistent. Unfortunately, in the absence of local small quarries working, it has also been used in villages that are traditionally of Inferior Oolite or Corallian limestones. The colour contrast is not compatible.

The working quarries in the Isle of Purbeck are often known by the names of the quarrymen and in 1996 the following were visible.

WORTH MATRAVERS

SY978781	(Name unknown)
SY978790	Southdown
SY978792	Downshay Wood
SY980791	Downs Quarry
SY981781	Eastington Farm
SY982783	(Name unknown)
SY982788	Sunnydown Farm
SY982794	Quarry Close
SY983790	Landers & Fratton
SY985781	Keates Quarry
SY986781	Cobb's Quarry

Bonfield's Quarry, Acton was working in 1997 in the Middle Purbeck limestones.

LANGTON MATRAVERS

SY980789	(Name unknown)
SY981785	Haysom's Acton Quarry
SY986780	Keates Quarry
SY987782	Lander's Acton Quarry
SY987783	Lovell's Acton Quarry
SY988782	Bonfield's Acton Quarry
SY988787	Bower's Acton Quarry
SY989782	D & P Lovell's Acton Quarry
SY990780	Lewis' Acton Quarry
SY991779	Blacklands
SY996778	Queensground
SY998792	Crack Lane Quarry

SWANAGE

SZ015774	Belle Vue Quarry
SZ019782	Higher Lanchards
SZ020780	Swanage quarries
SZ022776	California Farm
SZ023776	Southard
SZ026777	Townsend Quarry

Several of these are disused but still open, but it is official policy to backfill all working quarries and return to pasture. Keates' Quarry where dinosaur footprints were found, Queensground, Crack Lane and California Farm have all been designated as Regionally Important Geological Sites and so should remain open for scientific study. The exact site of working quarries changes as each patch is worked out, but all of the present workings are in the Middle Purbeck limestones. The site of any remaining Marble reserves is a closely guarded secret, and there is no current quarrying in the Broken Shell Limestone (Burr).

CHAPTER EIGHT

Cretaceous

WEALDEN

Geology

About 136 million years ago the arid environment of the Purbeck limestones gave way to wetter conditions and a river developed that ran from the west of England across the whole of Dorset, Hampshire and into Kent. This covered the Purbeck sediments in lake deposits that included thick beds of clay and various coloured sands. These Wealden sands, mostly unconsolidated, include heavy minerals from Dartmoor. Some remains of trees are found in the clays. About the middle of this sequence is a thick bed of coarse quartz grit coloured red.

Landscape

The Wealden sands and clays are only seen in Dorset in the valley between Worbarrow Bay and Swanage. The sequence is constantly eroding in Worbarrow Bay where it is exposed to the prevailing winds, and more slowly in the comparative shelter of Swanage Bay.

In this valley the Coarse Quartz Grit forms low hills that can best be seen at Corfe Common. The sandstone, which has been quarried on the Common,

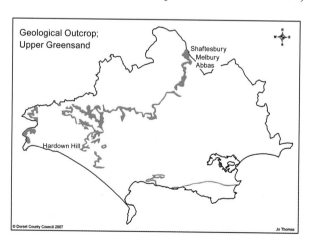

is a prominent ridge that supports a heathland type of vegetation, while the clays form the boggy low areas.

Use in Buildings

The Coarse Quartz Grit has been used in field walls in the Corfe valley, but all the buildings are of Purbeck limestone.

UPPER GREENSAND

Geology

About 112 million years ago, increased volcanic activity in the world's oceans began to cause a rise in world sea levels and to push the seawater over the land, flooding much of the European and American continents as the north Atlantic ocean widened. The first of the sediments deposited on the continental shelves at that time were the Lower Greensand, a poorly cemented sandy clay and the Gault clay, neither of use for building stone, though the Gault has been used for bricks.

As the sea rose over the land the deposits became more sandy and the Upper Greensand Formation was deposited. It includes various qualities of sand, coloured green by the presence of glauconite. Glauconite is a member of the mica mineral family, rich in iron but also containing potassium, magnesium and aluminium. It indicates marine deposition when little land-based sediment was available. The outcrops in West and North Dorset differ marginally in character, due to varying sea-floor conditions, including a shallower area in mid Dorset.

In West Dorset the lowest deposit in the Formation is a poorly cemented, fine-grained sand known as Foxmould, often used in mortar. Above this is a fossiliferous bed, then Chert Beds used for building in much the same way as flint, and finally the coarse-grained, well-cemented Eggardon Grit (named after the outcrop of rocks round the western end of Eggardon Hill). Chert differs from flint in having a granular texture. Both formed from the partly dissolved silica in sponge spicules or diatoms. In the Upper Greensand the silica has replaced the carbonate cement between the sand grains, leaving a granular texture. In the Chalk there is no sand present, so the calcium carbonate is entirely replaced, resulting in a pure silica flint with a glassy texture.

In North Dorset the lowest deposit is again a poorly cemented, fine-grained sand. Above this is the Shaftesbury Sandstone, a coarse green sandstone, often with random burrows. The sandstone has even-sized, sub-rounded, well sorted sand grains less than 1 millimetre in diameter, with open pore spaces, the fabric being grain supported. There is a small proportion of fine calcium carbonate cement. The glauconite grains that give it the green colour are the same size as the sand. The Chert Beds above are not used for building, and the Grit is not present. However, at the level of the Grit and possibly contemporaneous, the Melbury Sandstone coloured green with glauconite is quarried at Melbury Abbas. When freshly cut there appears to be more fine-grained calcium carbonate in the matrix than in the Shaftesbury Sandstone, and it is considered to be the lowest bed of the Chalk Group in that district.

At Bookham, near Alton Pancras, the Shaftesbury Sandstone can be seen in a cut face at the side of the farmyard. It is of interest as the top of the Sandstone has been eroded unevenly, as if worn away by wave action in shallow water on the mid-Dorset 'swell' area. On top of the sandstone the uneven surface has been re-covered by a conglomerate of broken sandstone and chalky mud now called the Bookham Conglomerate. Sea levels were rising again and this rough deposit is followed by deposition of the Lower Chalk. The sandstone has been used for building Bookham farmhouse.

Landscape

At the western edge of the Vale of Marshwood the Upper Greensand forms the capping to the flat-topped hills of Golden Cap, Langton Hill, Hardown Hill, Coney's Castle, Lambert's Castle, Blackdown, Pilsdon Pen and Lewesdon Hill. Langton Hill, Lambert's Castle and Lewesdon are remarkable for their

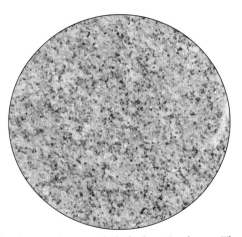

A sample of Upper Greensand Shaftesbury Sandstone. The green colour of the Upper Greensand Shaftesbury Sandstone is due to green crystals of glauconite, a complex mineral precipitated from sea-water in conditions not far from land (as seen through a handlens).

beechwoods, while Hardown has heathland, and Golden Cap and Pilsdon are bare.

The Upper Greensand is an excellent aquifer, providing much of the public water supply in Dorset. Spring lines occur at the base, especially where it is underlain by a clay, and this causes landslipping. Those hills topped by Upper Greensand therefore have steep sides, with boggy landslip areas at their feet.

The central Upper Greensand outcrop occurs around the lower slopes of the Chalk Downland, except at Shaftesbury, where the Chert Beds outcrop as a flat-topped hill. The steep-sided hill at Shaftesbury has been formed by landslipping, as the free-draining sandstone is underlain by Kimmeridge Clay, with the spring line undermining the Upper Greensand.

Quarrying and Use in Building

WEST DORSET

Hardown, Lamberts Castle and Blackdown all had many small quarries in the Chert Beds and Chert Drift. On Hardown Hill the mines are still open, and have provided homes for bats, so the entrance is covered by a locked grille. The quarries have been marked on nineteenth century OS maps, and many on an eighteenth century map known as a Terrier in private hands. The Shaftesbury Sandstone was mined or quarried from both sides of the hill (Wilderness, ST866221) and near Ivy Cross.

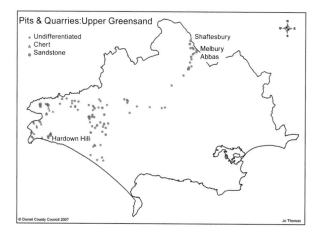

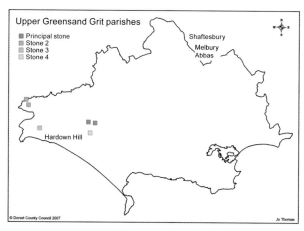

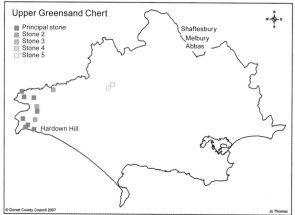

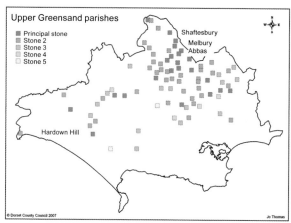

The Chert from Hardown Hill was taken as far as Exeter for roadstone, and has been used as a building material both in the core of walls and as a facing stone. It is used for walling around Charmouth and the Marshwood Vale. The lumps of Chert used at Thorncombe, from pits north of the village, appear to be larger than those used near Hardown Hill. The Chert was usually simply knapped to form a flat surface, but left rough round the natural edges. As chert lumps have uneven edges, it has been necessary to provide strengthening of cut stone at the quoins. It has been specially broken to form rectangles for the church at Catherston Leweston. The colour of the Chert for this polygonal walling has been carefully chosen to produce a silvery blue finish. At Forde Abbey both the Chert and a white sandstone associated with it have been brought from near Chard, Somerset for use in the thirteenth century monks dormitory and in the walls of the Norman

A chimney stack at Tempest House, close to Lambert's Castle, has been built of Upper Greensand chert.

Schematic section of Upper Greensand in West Dorset Not to scale

Eggardon Grit - coarse pale cream sandstone

Chert Beds - silver grey/blue chert nodules in fine sand

Exogyra Beds - fine sandstone with *Exogyra* and other fossils

Foxmould - fine pale green unconsolidated sand

Catherston Leweston church, built in 1858, has a polygonal exterior cladding of chert from the Upper Greensand of Hardown Hill. The chert is tan or silvery blue, much lighter in colour than flint from the Chalk.

A cottage in Whitchurch Canonicorum built with Upper Greensand chert from Hardown, with a later brick front.

chapel (1141). The Eggardon Grit has been used for building the barns at Toller Fratrum and at Lower Kingcombe.

In Charmouth and around the Marshwood Vale the Upper Greensand Chert is often used in the same buildings as the Lower Lias blue limestones. On the coast both the chert and the limestones may have been picked from the beach as cobbles, but inland the Belemnite Stone was dug from small pits in the Vale. The stones were bonded by clay from the fields.

Bricks were made at the Mutton Street brickworks from the late seventeenth century and into the nineteenth century, using the Belemnite Marls. These were used in several villages including Whitchurch Canonicorum, where a pair of cottages is faced with bricks, but has chert at the sides.

The 16th century stable block at Toller Fratrum has been built of Upper Greensand grit and chert, Chalk block, and some brick at the rear with Ham Hill Stone window mullions.

On Gold Hill, Shaftesbury, the central area of the retaining wall is built directly on the Upper Greensand Shaftesbury Sandstone. The top of Shaftesbury hill is crowned by the Chert beds known as the Boyne Hollow Chert, consisting of chert nodules surrounded by loose sand – hence the need for a retaining wall when the roadway was widened to accommodate the market.

The Cerne and Piddle valleys are close to the central 'swell' area of Dorset where the Upper Greensand was deposited over a marine ridge, with basins on either side. The sequence of beds and their character are therefore rather different. At Minterne Parva, the Shaftesbury Sandstone has become rubbly and is only used as coursed rubble in the house and farm.

The houses in the Pump Yard, St. James, Shaftesbury, are built of the Shaftesbury Sandstone from quarries in the sides of the hill.

Schematic section of Upper Greensand in North Dorset   Not to scale

Melbury Sandstone - glauconitic fine-grained sandstone (within Chalk Group)

Chert Beds - grey chert nodules in fine sand

Shaftesbury Sandstone - glauconitic fine-grained sandstone

Cann Sand - fine unconsolidated sand

NORTH DORSET

The Shaftesbury Sandstone is an excellent building stone that can be cut as ashlar and is extensively used in the Stour valley as far south as Spetisbury. As well as domestic and church buildings, it has proved suitable for bridges because it can withstand constant immersion in water. The Saxon abbey at Shaftesbury, founded in 880, was built on a foundation of the Chert Beds, using loose boulders of Shaftesbury Sandstone from the hillsides. This stone was re-used for the town after the Dissolution of the Monasteries. Quarries were also cut into both sides of the hilltop, and can still be seen at Wilderness. Two quarries are shown on a map of the town drawn by Upjohn in 1799, and quarrying continued until 1888. The beds have been described by the British Geological Survey as a weakly-cemented lower sandstone, with a hard shelly calcite-cemented glauconitic sandstone in the upper part. This upper bed was previously known as the Ragstone.

Sandstone from Shaftesbury has also been used at Ashmore, Cann and Compton Abbas and in the Iwerne and Tarrant valleys. The tithe barn at Iwerne Courtney has a Greensand and flint exterior, with a lining of Chalk. The exterior of the church is

The exterior of the tithe barn at Iwerne Courtney was built of Upper Greensand Shaftesbury Sandstone and flint, the interior being lined with Chalk block from quarries in the Lower Chalk on Hambledon Hill.

Above The front of Pond House in Ashmore is entirely built of Shaftesbury Sandstone in various sized blocks.

Left A sample of Melbury Sandstone quarried on Melbury Farm in 2004. The new supermarket in Shaftesbury has decorations of this stone (as seen through a handlens).

of Corallian limestone, flint and Chalk block. Cross House in Fontmell Magna (late sixteenth century) has Upper Greensand on the lower part of the façade, with Corallian Todber Freestone above and on the gable ends. Sutton Waldron and the Iwernes have the same mixture. From Shaftesbury, the stone has been carried to Sturminster Newton and Blandford

Greensand, while the churchyard and estate walls have a mixture of Greensand, Chalk and Corallian from Marnhull.

The Boyne Hollow Chert, above the Shaftesbury Sandstone, is not used for building. The Melbury Sandstone, a fine-grained, calcareous, glauconitic sandstone occurs above the chert at Melbury Abbas, at a similar level to the Eggardon Grit of West Dorset. It is very similar to the Shaftesbury Sandstone and therefore it is difficult to distinguish the two in a building, but has certainly been used in its own village. It has recently (2004) been used for decoration of the Tesco supermarket in Shaftesbury.

Other quarries existed as far south as Fontmell Magna, but the stone becomes too soft for building further south. Fontmell Magna also has buildings

19th century cottages in Fontmell Magna have been built of Shaftesbury Sandstone, flint and ironstone chequer, with brick dressings. Brick was made locally from the Gault Clay.

Sturminster Newton Town Bridge, on the river Stour, is built of Upper Greensand Shaftesbury Sandstone. The walls of the mill nearby that stand in the river are also Greensand. Corallian limestone is more readily available for building in Sturminster Newton, but it is not suitable for walls that stand in water.

churches that are almost entirely of Shaftesbury Sandstone, and to the fifteenth century towers at Child Okeford, Okeford Fitzpaine and Durweston.

Moving south and east from Shaftesbury down the Tarrant valley flint is used with the Upper Greensand, with the proportion of heathstone increasing downstream. The Greensand has been used in the towers of Tarrant Rushton (fourteenth century) and Witchampton (fifteenth century) churches. In Woodlands parish, south of Cranborne, Woodlands farm has a sixteenth century retaining wall containing large dressed blocks of Upper Greensand and heathstone. Knowlton church (fourteenth century) is built of flint, heathstone, and Greensand.

GREENSAND FROM WILTSHIRE

In North and East Dorset another Greensand is used in domestic buildings and bridges. It is finer grained, often pale green, or even hardly green at all. This is the same age as Portland Sand and has been quarried from mines in Chilmark and Tisbury in the Vale of Wardour. A white limestone of the same age as the Portland Freestone beds on Portland was also quarried. The sandstone is found in Cranborne Manor, in the entrance lodge to Crichel House at Witchampton, and was used in Eastbury.

The carvings from Shaftesbury Abbey now in the Abbey Museum are more likely to be the white limestone from Chilmark. Wimborne Minster also has pale sandstone in the west tower that probably came from the Vale of Wardour.

The design of the church at Horton, built in 1722-55 at the same time as the grand mansion at Eastbury, shows Vanbrugh's influence on the builder John Chapman. The stone includes Upper Greensand ashlar, in the chancel, north wall and tower. The doorway is of dressed stone from the Vale of Wardour. On the west wall the Greensand is mixed with ironstone found locally, some knapped flint and a few dressed blocks of Purbeck Burr and Marble, probably from an earlier building. The south and west walls are of brick similar to the vicarage next door, with eighteenth century windows. This brick would have been made locally from Reading Beds clay.

CHALK
Geology

As the sea deepened, about 99 million years ago, deposition began of the fine-grained remains of a microscopic plankton known as coccoliths. The skeletons of this plankton formed hollow balls consisting of plate-like crystals of calcite. It is

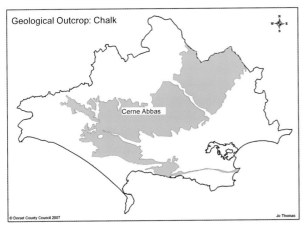

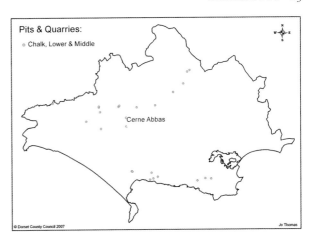

The apparent gaps in the Chalk downland are river valleys where the Chalk is covered in alluvium.

thought that the plankton initially formed the food of crustaceans, the remains being deposited as waste. The lowest beds of the Chalk still contain some sand and scattered grains of glauconite. The Lower Chalk is now about 57 metres thick. Beer Stone is of this age, but differs from the Chalk in Dorset with the inclusion of echinoid (sea urchin) debris.

The sea continued to deepen until it reached about 300 metres and covered a wide area of western Europe and North America. The Middle Chalk (93.5 million years ago) has scattered flint nodules and a nodular appearance. The flint is thought to have formed from the silica of sponge spicules, or of diatoms. Middle Chalk is about 41 metres thick.

The Upper Chalk was deposited between 89 and 71 million years ago. It is more smooth in appearance, and the flint nodules are often in lines, as if on a bedding surface. The nodules' uneven shape could be due to a silica gel filling burrows left by crustaceans. The Upper Chalk is not complete in Dorset, possibly because it was eroded away, but is still 260 metres thick. Apart from the lowest beds of Chalk, containing some sand, the whole depth is homogeneous, suggesting that marine conditions varied little over 28 million years.

Landscape

While the Upper Greensand tops the hills on the western side of the Marshwood Vale, the Chalk tops the eastern hills. Between Rampisham and Bulbarrow the Chalk Downland is cut by steep-sided valleys in which the streams run north/south and the main roads run north/south on the ridges.

The Chalk Downland forms a broad sweep across central Dorset from the coast at White Nothe to Melbury Down on the Wiltshire border. This downland forms the high ground on the southern and eastern side of the Blackmore Vale, the scarp edges being cut into steep sided valleys during the last ice age. The Chalk dips at a low angle to the southeast, with streams draining the hillsides into the river Stour. The Stour has cut through the scarp face of the Chalk at Blandford, due to a line of weakness on a fault.

A narrow ridge runs from the coast at White Nothe, west to east across the Isle of Purbeck. Between Worbarrow and Swanage the Chalk has been pushed almost vertical by continental pressure from the south. There are many faults cutting across the Chalk ridge that appear to be in pairs, one fault trending north-east/south-west, the other north-west/south-east.

A block of the Lower Chalk from the Old Bell has scattered dark crystals of glauconite among the fine chalk (as seen through a handlens).

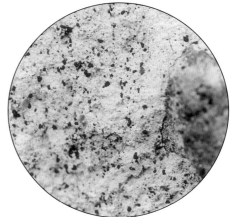

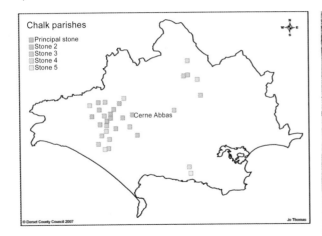

Chalk parishes
■ Principal stone
■ Stone 2
■ Stone 3
■ Stone 4
■ Stone 5

Cerne Abbas

© Dorset County Council 2007

Jo Thomas

The North Barn of the Abbey at Cerne Abbas, now Beauvoir Court, has an outer wall of large blocks of Middle Chalk from the quarry on the south side of Giant Hill.

Quarrying and Use in Building

The Lower Chalk has been used for building in Cerne Abbas, Sydling St. Nicholas and Cattistock. Its gritty texture makes the Chalk look grey.

Cerne Abbey was originally Anglo-Saxon and probably mainly built of wood, but the Normans built in stone. Only four buildings remain relatively intact. The remains of the Abbey are now simply banks in the field below Giant Hill. The tithe barn is now a private house separated from the village and therefore difficult to see. The fifteenth century Hospice, or lodging house, has exterior walls of flint banded with Purbeck limestone, and some Ham Hill Stone windows and quoins. The oriel window at the side is mostly constructed of Portland stone. The walls are lined with Chalk block. The gatehouse, or Abbot's porch, built 1497-1509, has walls of Ham Hill Stone and Portland limestone. The other building remaining intact, though much altered, is

The remains of Cerne Abbey are now simply lumps in a field

North Barn, now called Beauvoir Court. This was originally built in the fifteenth century of large nodular Chalk blocks containing scattered lumps of flint. This is characteristic of the Middle Chalk. Such large blocks of stone must have come from the quarry on the south east side of Giant Hill.

Abbey Farm, at the end of the Pitchmarket, incorporates part of the abbey buildings, but most had to be rebuilt after a fire. The walls are of Purbeck limestone and flint. In Long Street, to the south of the New Inn, is a terrace of chequered houses built in the late nineteenth century of knapped flint and Chalk block walls on an ashlar plinth. Ham Hill Stone has been used for the quoins. The front wall of the New Inn is a patchwork of brick and stone. At the right hand end a mixture of stone including Ham Hill Stone (orange), Chalk (white), Purbeck (small, white/light grey) and flint goes up to the roof. Below the windows the stone is mainly the small blocks of Purbeck, with the mix as before between them. The window surrounds are of Ham Hill Stone. At the left hand end the striped appearance is created by flint banded with Chalk. The Chalk has a greyish look, and contains scattered crystals of glauconite (dark green). On the left corner, above head height, a block of Chalk has weathered so that a *Calycoceras* ammonite and an *Inoceramus* bivalve can be seen. Stone tiles on the roof are from Purbeck and weigh 230 tons. The barns at the rear have more Chalk and flint and a carving referred to as 'Catherine' wheels from the Abbey is leaning against the back wall of the Inn.

The walls of the New Inn in Cerne Abbas include Chalk block, flint, Lower Purbeck limestone and flint, with Ham Hill Stone round the windows and Purbeck roof tiles.

The Old Bell in Cerne Abbas has Lower Purbeck below the windows, flint and Lower Chalk above. The lower window mullions are of Ham Hill Stone.

A side wall of the next house has Greensand, Chalk and Ham Hill Stone with flint, but the front is brick. The next stone house is the Old Bell at no. 20. Below the windows the wall is of Purbeck limestone, whose thinly bedded weathering is characteristic of stone from the Ridgeway quarries in the Lower Purbeck. From the windows upwards flint is banded with the greyish Lower Chalk. The glauconite crystals are visible, with some phosphatic nodules and at least one specimen of *Turrilites acutus*. This identified the Chalk as being Cenomanian, the Zig Zag Chalk, which would have been quarried from Giant Hill. The lower windows are of Ham Hill Stone. The house next to the Old Bell has painted rubble walls at the side and the rear range is of cob, with an earth floor. 'Earth' does not mean simply soil, but is made of Chalk crushed and beaten smooth.

The Royal Oak Inn was built in the early sixteenth century, while the Abbey was still standing. Its walls are of flint and rubble which may include Upper Greensand. The village is built in a valley on an outcrop of Upper Greensand. St. Mary's church was started in 1300, the nave and south porch being fifteenth century, and the west tower 1500. The tower and entrance porch are of Ham Hill Stone, with the plinth of the nave being of Ham Hill Stone and Portland limestone ashlar. The nineteenth century south wall of the nave is banded with small blocks of Purbeck limestone, then ashlar blocks of Ham Hill Stone and Portland limestone banded with flint.

Opposite the church the Pitchmarket, built in

about 1500, has stone walls of flint banded with stone, both Purbeck and Ham Hill Stone, and timber frame above. In front of this row of houses the cobbles are of flint. It is most likely that all the flint used in the village has come from the Clay with Flints on top of the surrounding hills. The pinkish 'rind' on the cobbles is staining from the minerals within the clay.

The many blocks of Chalk seen in various buildings are somewhat whiter than the grey, glauconitic Chalk from the Zig Zag Chalk used in the New Inn and the Old Bell. They may therefore come from the higher

The south side of the nave of Cerne Abbas church has been built of Ham Hill Stone, flint, some Portland Freestone and smaller blocks of Purbeck limestone.

parts of the old quarry in the New Pit Chalk. The nodular Chalk in the North Barn would be from the Holywell Nodular Chalk in between. The huge size of the quarry would suggest that far more Chalk has been used in the village buildings, or perhaps in other villages, than can be seen from the street.

The Purbeck limestone is recognisable by comparison with the limestones used from Weymouth northwards. It weathers in a totally different way from the Middle Purbeck limestones quarried in the Isle of Purbeck. The Portland ashlar seen in the church, the Hospice and the Abbot's Porch is similar in character to the Portland ashlar used for the abbey at Abbotsbury. At Abbotsbury this has been positively identified as coming from Portesham quarry, the westernmost quarry on the Ridgeway. However there are other quarries on the Ridgeway where Portland limestone of similar character is available. It is recorded that the original Anglo-Saxon Cerne Abbey owned Poxwell, where the quarry is the easternmost of the Ridgeway series. Most of the Ridgeway quarries have been cut through both the Lower Purbeck and the Portland limestones.

Chalk block used for building was often known as Clunch. Although only a small number of buildings have Chalk on the outside, as it often proved too soft to survive weathering, many buildings in the Chalk Downland area have used it for interior walls. The great barn at Iwerne Courtney, whose outside walls are Shaftesbury Sandstone and flint, is lined with Chalk. Several inner walls in Blandford, a town rebuilt in brick after an eighteenth century fire, have been seen during recent renovation to be of Chalk. In Coombe Keynes the Purbeck and heathstone cottages sometimes have Chalk block inner walls.

At Hooke most Chalk cottages have been demolished and rebuilt using Inferior Oolite. At Cattistock many cottages have been rendered and

Top The churchyard wall in Iwerne Courtney has been built of Chalk block from Hambledon Hill and orange Corallian limestone from Marnhull or Todber.

Middle The estate wall in Iwerne Courtney includes Chalk, Corallian limestone, Upper Greensand Shaftesbury Sandstone and flint. The roof of the wall is a sandstone that may have come from the Corallian beds, but sandstone from the Forest Marble is also possible.

Bottom The barn at Baglake Farm, Long Bredy, has Corallian limestone from a quarry on the farm, with Chalk block from Litton Cheney parish pit above.

Above A cottage of Chalk block in Cattistock.

Left An echinoid (sea urchin) spine can be seen in a block of Lower Chalk in the wall of the Fox and Hounds in Cattistock.

of those left uncovered some are weathering badly. As Chalk is porous, house walls are usually built on a plinth of less porous stone, such as flint, Forest Marble or Corallian limestones. At least two different Chalk ammonites can be seen in the wall of the Fox and Hounds, Cattistock, with a small echinoid spine. At Toller Fratrum the farmhouse (1540) is built of Chalk block, Inferior Oolite, Upper Greensand Grit and Ham Hill Stone. It previously had a roof of Forest Marble siltstone tiles. The barn walls are of Upper Greensand, Chalk block and flint. A late eighteenth century farm building at Iwerne Stepleton also uses Chalk block.

In the western area of Chalk downland, Askerswell is close enough to Loders to be built mostly of Inferior Oolite, but Church Farm (late seventeenth century) has Chalk block on the front wall. At Litton Cheney the contrast in the barn at Baglake Farm is striking, with orange Corallian limestone in the lower half and Chalk block above.

On the Chalk Downland crushed Chalk was also used for cob, mixed with straw or cow-hair and cow dung. Chalk cob walls surround the walled garden at Cranborne Manor, Edmondsham House and some farm buildings in Shapwick. The cob was originally painted with limewash or a mixture of limewash and tallow to keep it waterproof, and the top of free-standing walls was tiled or thatched. Most cob walls in cottages are now rendered, but renovations to one at Turnworth showed its construction.

FLINT

Geology

Flint, found as nodules in the Middle and Upper Chalk, is a form of silica that has hardened as a glassy lump, rather than forming separate crystals. In the Middle Chalk the nodules are random, but in the Upper Chalk the nodules often form horizontal lines. They may be the remains of sponges or diatoms that have filled in burrows left by crustaceans, or hollow fossils such as echinoids.

Continued continental movement pushed the Chalk above sea level, and by 40 million years ago weathering had begun to break it down. Flint, being extremely hard, has survived as part of the Clay with Flints found on the top of parts of the Chalk Downlands. During the last Ice Age extreme

Though older buildings used knapped flint in rough shapes, the Victorians tended to square up the nodules as in Winterborne Zelston church (1865).

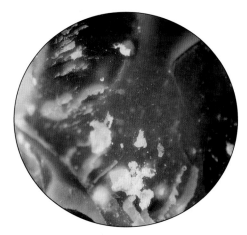

Flint has a glassy texture and is black or brown in colour. It is found in the Middle and Upper Chalk, as well as in loose nodules in later deposits weathered from the Chalk (as seen through a handlens).

weathering has broken the nodules into smaller pieces in the Terrace Gravels, but some echinoids still remain recognisable. Fresh flint is black or dark brown, but exposure to the light over many centuries tends to fade the darker colours. Each nodule has an outer porcellanous (chalky) crust that is originally white, but the minerals in the Clay with Flints have stained this crust pink, and in the Terrace Gravels it has been stained orange by iron oxides.

Quarrying and Use in Buildings

Flint for building has been gathered from ploughed fields directly above the Chalk, being either picked by hand or swept up when harrowing the fields; or separated from the Clay with Flints when the clay was being prepared for brickmaking. It has been extensively used throughout the whole Chalk Downland area. It is a durable building material, but its uneven shape means that the structural support of a building, such as the quoins at the corners, as well as door and window surrounds, must be made of stone or brick. To provide strength throughout the wall, flint is often used banded or chequered with stone or brick. The stone used will depend on the nearest source. At Ashmore it is used with Upper Greensand. At Bere Regis and in the Piddle and Cerne valleys it is banded or chequered with Purbeck limestone.

The nodules are most often split to produce a flat face, sometimes knapped square, or for rough walling used whole. Victorian masons knapped flint square to produce a characteristically ordered appearance to the buildings, as seen in Winterborne Zelston church. To roughly split nodules of flint, they can be put in a sack and hammered, but knapping is a skill that requires a glancing blow with another piece of flint, to break off rough edges. This method was used to make sharp flint arrowheads and axeheads from the flakes broken off, in the Neolithic. The Victorian squared flints required a high degree of skill.

Although flint is the most important building material on the central Chalk downland, each river valley draining the downland has its own particular mixture of building materials, depending on its distance from the source of good building stone.

In the Frome valley Knapp Farm (1580) near Benville Bridge, is built close to springs issuing from the Upper Greensand. The front of the house is of Forest Marble, with Ham Hill Stone window mullions. At the back rubble of Upper Greensand, flint, Chalk block, Forest Marble and Cornbrash is used for the exterior walls. The inner walls are of Chalk block. Near Cattistock the building accounts of Chantmarle House are of the part built for Sir John Strode between 1612 and 1615 of Ham Hill Stone. He recorded that Joseph & Daniel Rower of Hambdon Hill, Somerset, took the building of the walls to 'wask-work at 20d a perch for the first story and 2s a perch for the two upper stories'. Wask-work was a form of tooling and a perch was approximately 5 metres in length. The cost of the whole house amounted to £1142. ('besides much stone, many timber trees, and a very great number of carriages of stones, both from Hambdon and Whetley quarries

Cottages in Tarrant Gunville built of flint, greensand and brick.

(Inferior Oolite), freely given me by my neighbours, especially of Beminster and Netherbury'). The fifteenth century west wing and sixteenth century south wing are of flint banded with Forest Marble limestones and sandstones.

Both the fifteenth century and nineteenth century parts of Maiden Newton church are built of flint and Purbeck limestone from the Ridgeway quarries. The Victorian work is neatly banded. In the villages closer to Dorchester, such as Frampton and Charminster, the flint is mixed with stone from the Portland and Purbeck quarries on the Ridgeway.

In the upper part of the Piddle valley the cottages are built of flint and brick or Purbeck stone from the Ridgeway. The majority of Piddletrenthide church was built during the fifteenth century with flint and Ham Hill Stone. The *Dorset County Chronicle* of 13th February 1868 reported that Piddlehinton church was restored using flint banded with Ridgeway (Portland or Purbeck) stone. Below Dorchester in the Piddle valley Affpuddle has a wide range of building materials, with cottages of cob, brick, flint and heathstone.

The Stour valley north of Blandford has good building stone from Shaftesbury and the Marnhull to Todber area. In Fontmell Magna and Sutton Waldron these are mixed with flint. In Iwerne Courtney (Shroton) the cottages next to the church and the churchyard boundary wall are a mixture of Chalk block, Corallian limestone, flint and Upper Greensand. Flint is also used with Greensand in Stourpaine. The churches at Spetisbury and Charlton Marshall have been built of a mix of Upper Greensand and flint, with heathstone and Purbeck limestone at Shapwick.

The River Tarrant flows into the Stour, and the villages in the Tarrant valley all use flint mixed with Upper Greensand or heathstone in their cottages and churches.

Cranborne Chase has many villages where flint is used in company with Upper Greensand from Shaftesbury, or the Greensand from the Vale of Wardour known as Chilmark Stone. These include Ashmore, Farnham, Chettle, Sixpenny Handley, Gussage All Saints and Gussage St. Michael.

CHAPTER NINE

Tertiary Heathstone

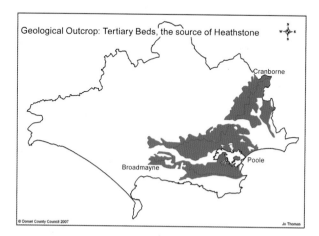

Geological Outcrop: Tertiary Beds, the source of Heathstone

Cranborne

Broadmayne

Poole

© Dorset County Council 2007

Jo Thomas

The Tertiary London Clay and Poole Formation form a continuous outcrop from Broadmayne to Cranborne across the whole of south east Dorset, but the apparent gaps in this map are due to cover by alluvium or river terrace gravel in the valleys and a wide spread of terrace gravels in the Poole and Bournemouth area.

GEOLOGY

About 65 million years ago, continental movement caused the western European continental shelf to rise above sea level and for about 15 million years the Chalk-covered landscape of Dorset was subject to weathering and erosion. This removed a good thickness of the Upper Chalk in Dorset, though more remains in south east England, due to the south-easterly dip of the beds. Sea levels rose again about 50 million years ago, and the early Tertiary Reading Beds and London Clay were deposited on an irregular eroded Chalk surface as sea levels fluctuated. Their outcrop now runs in an arc from near Lulworth through Bere Regis and north of Wimborne to Cranborne. Though mostly clays, there are several pebble beds consisting of rounded beach pebbles, and sands. There are two iron-rich sandstones recently named the Lytchett Matravers Sandstone and the sandstone within Warmwell Farm sand by the British Geological Survey. These has been mapped

Pieces of the Poole Formation sandstone are scattered all over Hartland Moor. The sandstone strengthens the tops of all the hills, and was previously dug from small scrapes such as this tiny pit.

The Lytchett Matravers Sandstone from the London Clay, has rounded, iron-coated grains of sand with few pore spaces. This block is in the eastern wall of the chancel at Lytchett Matravers church.

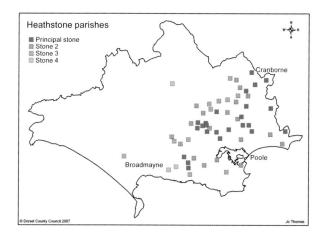

Heathstone parishes
- Principal stone
- Stone 2
- Stone 3
- Stone 4

Cranborne

Broadmayne

Poole

© Dorset County Council 2007   Jo Thomas

with the Tertiary, and the sarsens found in several valleys on the Chalk downland may have formed at that time.

About 1.8 million years ago, during the Ice Ages, deep weathering of the Chalk and the outwash of rivers in tundra-like conditions, added spreads of flint gravel over the Tertiary sediments.

LANDSCAPE

The acid nature of the gravels and the Tertiary sands and clays has given rise to heathland over the whole of south east Dorset. The Ice Ages alternated between frozen tundra and much warmer conditions during which the main rivers, the Frome, Stour and Avon, have cut down through the gravels and into the sands and clays. This has resulted in flat-topped gravel-spread hills with terraces down the sides showing when erosion slowed for a while. There are wide valleys where the gravel has been eroded away, such as Poole where the heights of Broadstone and Parkstone have retained their gravel spreads. Between the Frome and the Piddle the ridge of gravel at Culpepper's Dish has collapsed into a doline (a cone-shaped deep hole) caused by solution of the Chalk perhaps 100 metres beneath. The Tertiary sands are exposed in the lower heathland.

The cliffs of Poole Bay and Christchurch Bay have up to 2 metres of gravel at the top, with the Poole Formation, Branksome Sands and Barton Beds underneath, changing in an easterly direction.

Most of Lytchett Matravers church is built of local sandstone from the London Clay with rounded grains. A 20th century addition on the north is from the Poole Formation at Henbury sandpit.

in isolated patches around Lytchett Matravers and north of Wimborne. Iron-rich sandstones occur in places over the whole outcrop, but are not named, or even mapped elsewhere.

The following Eocene sediments (Poole Formation, Branksome Sand and Barton Beds) were deposited by a river running from the west of England into an estuary that reached the sea east of the Isle of Wight. The river appears to have changed its course many times as it meandered over a wide, flat plain. The outcrop is found east of the London Clay outcrop, with younger sediments on top as one moves in a south-easterly direction.

At that time, about 40 to 35 million years ago, the high ground of the Chalk Purbeck Hills and the Chalk on the Isle of Wight was joined, forming a southern boundary to the river valley. The Poole Formation is a series of sands and clays, with occasional lenses of iron-rich sandstone. The sand parts of the series are thicker than the clays, and have been named for the districts in which they occur on the surface – Creekmoor, Oakdale, Broadstone and Parkstone. The Branksome Sand (also named after its district) has some sandy clay, with lenses of iron-rich sandstone above. At the base of the Barton Clays is a fine iron-rich sandstone, seen on Hengistbury Head as lines of large nodules in the cliff. This contained such a good proportion of iron that it was mined as iron ore. The Barton Beds are the youngest of the Tertiary sediments in Dorset and are about 37 million years old.

It is possible that Tertiary sediments were originally on top of the Chalk much further west than the present outcrop. The deep gravel deposit on Black Down by Hardy's Monument has been dated

Above The barn at Old Park Farm, Lytchett Matravers, is built of the stone on which it stands – the Lytchett Matravers Sandstone.

Below Coombe Keynes church tower was built of Lower Purbeck Cypris Freestone from the Ridgeway quarries, and iron-cemented sandstone from the London Clay found in the village.

Above Almer church has dark sandstone from the London Clay in the tower and chancel, and similar stone with rounded grains but a lighter colour in the south wall of the nave. Judging by the shape of the windows, this is a later construction.

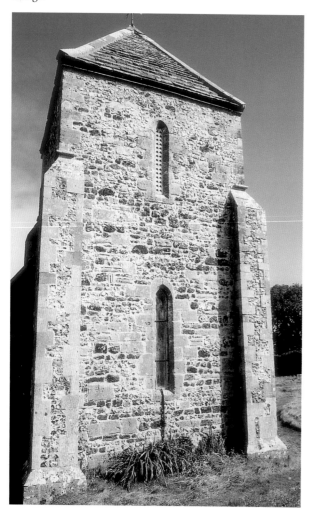

QUARRYING AND USE IN BUILDING

All the Tertiary clays have been used in brickmaking, especially during the nineteenth and early twentieth centuries. The sands are still being used for building purposes, in mortar, or in cement. Only the iron-rich sandstones have been used as building stones in their own right. They are known locally and collectively as ' heathstones'.

The British Geological Survey have mapped several pits in the Lytchett Matravers area that may have been dug for building stone. The Lytchett Matravers sandstone has been used without doubt in Lytchett Matravers church, and in Almer church. At Lytchett Matravers it is a dark brown colour, but at Almer the south wall is a lighter orange/brown. The barn at Old Park Farm, Lytchett Matravers, stands on an outcrop of the Lytchett Matravers sandstone and is therefore an example of the particular nature of the stone. The grains of sand are completely rounded and covered by the iron deposit. Other buildings in Lytchett Matravers include sandstone in which the grains are not completely rounded, and not all covered by the iron deposit. These probably came from the Warmwell Farm Sand.

The limited area in which the Lytchett Matravers Sandstone has been mapped by the BGS, and the age of the buildings in which it has been identified with confidence suggest that any quarries would be

Sandstone from the Poole Formation contains sub-rounded grains, some of which are clear rather than iron-coated. The pore spaces are only partly filled with finer sand (as seen through a handlens).

hard to find. However, the well cemented nature of the sandstone suggests that it would be found in the medieval bridges, if they can be examined closely. There may be some pieces in Sturminster Marshall and Shapwick churches, the remains of Tarrant Abbey at Tarrant Crawford, and Tarrant Rushton church.

In Chalbury, Horton and Woodlands, as well as in Knowlton church and Cranborne, iron-rich sandstone has been used in combination with other stones. The Lytchett Matravers sandstone is mapped as far north as Holt, but the British Geological Survey Ringwood sheet further north makes no mention of it. The only sandstone mapped is a ' glauconitic sand' . Careful examination of the heathstone in the

buildings suggests that this is all Poole Formation. However a marker stone in Church Street, Cranborne, that includes the characteristic rounded pebbles of the local London Clay/Reading Beds, has rounded almost black grains, with the same colour cement.

At the western end of the London Clay outcrop, in Coombe Keynes, lumps of ironstone appear in the sand of the gardens on the London Clay. Blocks of this ironstone, some with the characteristic rounded pebbles, are used in the church and in the cottages and garden walls. However, some of the Victorian rebuild has ironstone with ' sharp' sand grains.

The Poole Formation sandstone only occurs in patches and has been collected as a sideline from sandpits, or simply picked from ploughed fields. The only source at present (2007) is in the Henbury sandpit between Corfe Mullen and Lytchett Matravers (Sturminster Marshall parish). Here it occurs in one area of the pit, at the level of the Broadstone Sand. At its thickest it is 2 metres thick, but it fades out rapidly into clay at the edges.

The difference between the two sandstones on a microscopic scale in individual blocks is difficult to state with confidence. The Lytchett Matravers sand grains are rounded, grain sizes 0.2 to 0.3 millimetres. The Poole Formation sand grains are sharp edged to sub-rounded, and though some blocks have grains about 0.3 millimetres, there is a great variation in grain size up to 1.0 millimetre. Both vary in colour from dark brown to light tan in the East Dorset area. The Poole Formation south of Wareham varies through all the browns with an almost blood red

Holme Bridge was built of Purbeck limestone with some local Poole Formation heathstone and a later parapet of brick.

Above The construction of Wimborne Minster has taken place over many centuries. It therefore includes most of the building materials available in eastern Dorset. Purbeck limestone would have come up the river Stour, having been brought from the Isle of Purbeck by sea. Portland limestone from the Purbeck cliffs would have come the same way. The brown stone is heathstone, mostly from the Poole Formation heaths to the south of the river, but some has rounded grains that suggest the London Clay sandstone to the north of the town.

Below Heathstone blocks in Sturminster Marshall church. Some of the blocks in the church have rounded grains, some are sharper sand.

tone around Studland. In the Poole Formation, the pore spaces are often open, though just as often filled, whereas in the Lytchett Matravers sandstone they are always filled with an almost black cement.

Squared rubble from the Broadstone Sand has been used in the Studland area. There are the remains of quarries in the Poole Formation Broadstone Sand on Woodhouse Hill (SZ029821) and south of the Studland golf course (SZ012822). The colour and grain-size variations contrast with the Lytchett Matravers sandstone. The Norman church in Studland is mostly built of Purbeck limestone, but the walls include some of this Broadstone Sand. The church at Arne is mostly heathstone from the Poole Formation, but also has some Purbeck limestone.

At Canford Magna the church tower is of heathstone, while the main church is a mixture of heathstone and Purbeck limestone. On the south wall much of the rubble has inclusions of orange clay, which also appears in King John's kitchen. Kinson church tower was built in the twelfth century of heathstone ashlar in large blocks that appear current bedded. Most of the heathstone in Sturminster

Marshall and Shapwick churches is sharp-grained. The nineteenth century church at Morden, although so close to Lytchett Matravers, appears to be sharp-grained Poole Formation.

In the lower Frome valley Bindon Abbey was built of an iron-rich sandstone, which is also in the church at Wool and East Holme. While the former may be from the London Clay, the last is definitely from the Poole Formation and is also recorded as being used in the Butevant tower of Corfe Castle.

Wimborne Minster, originally founded in the seventh century but enlarged and rebuilt many times, has a good deal of 'heathstone' in its outer walls. A few blocks when viewed through a hand-lens show rounded grains of sand of an even size, the grains themselves dark coloured, grain-supported with little cement. Other blocks, when similarly viewed, show sub-rounded grains of varying sizes, mostly uncoloured, with finer sand grains forming the cement. Some is squared rubble, some is cut as ashlar from a current-bedded sandstone. In the twelfth century wall of the south aisle Poole Formation sandstone has inclusions of orange clay, similar to Canford Magna.

In the west corner of the north transept an Anglo-Saxon turret is entirely of heathstone. The Normans continued to use heathstone in the thirteenth century for the north transept. The fourteenth north porch has

Most of the cottages in Sturminster Marshall are built of brick, but Keystone Cottage has lower courses of heathstone.

mostly heathstone, mixed with Purbeck limestone. The central tower is a fine mixture of heathstone and Purbeck limestone. In the thirteenth and fourteenth century the south transept and the chancel were built of heathstone and Purbeck limestone. The south transept also includes Portland limestone. The south

The barn at Tarrant Crawford may have been part of the 12th century Abbey. The construction includes Purbeck limestone and heathstone.

Fingermarks can be seen in the leper window of Tarrant Rushton church which was built of heathstone.

vestry, built in the fourteenth century, is of Purbeck Burr limestone. Viewed from the north the Minster looks mostly brown with a speckled tower. Viewed from the south, the grey of the Purbeck and Portland limestones predominates.

When the west tower was built in the fifteenth century its exterior was of Greensand, with only a few blocks of heathstone and Portland stone. However, Hutchins (III, p 206) records that in 1447 John Benton, lord of the manor of Hampreston, gave permission for his parishioners to gather 200 loads of stone from any part of all the common heath belonging to Hampreston specifically for the tower. No stone from the Hampreston area is visible, but it could have been used for the interior of the 2 metres thick walls, as rubble between the inner and outer walls.

The types of stone available in Hampreston parish are the Terrace Gravels, which could have included sarsens and the London Clay to the north that could include the Lytchett Matravers Sandstone. Towards Ferndown and Stapehill the Broadstone Sand might have included the iron-cemented heathstone.

The north wall of St. George's Chapel in the Minster was rebuilt in 1855 in the same manner as the church hall next door. The heathstone for the hall is recorded as coming from Woodhouse Hill in Studland, now identified as the Broadstone Sand of the Poole Formation. The sand in all these heathstones appears sharp, and some of the blocks include blebs of clay, so that a local source in the heathlands to the south and east based on the Poole Formation is most likely.

As dressed stone the heathstone has been carried some distance from the heathland areas because its rich colour was highly prized. At Tarrant Rushton (twelfth century) the cruciform church has a window on the north side, with a view of the altar through a hagioscope, built of heathstone and showing the marks of the fingers of lepers from a nearby hospital.

From Throop downstream on the River Stour the ironstone takes on a different character to the Lytchett Matravers Sandstone (London Clay) and the ironstone from the Poole Formation. Here it has a finer grain size and the colour is blood-red to purple. A row of cottages at Holdenhurst has been built of stone from the medieval church, and in Christchurch the Priory ruins, the castle and the Constable's house all contain examples of ironstone, mixed with the limestones from Purbeck. This ironstone is from Hengistbury Head, where the boulders fall to the beach as the cliff erodes, and were used in these older buildings.

CHAPTER TEN

Stone Bridges of the Stour Valley

During the course of my explorations in Dorset I found that Hutchins in his *History of Dorset* had listed all the stone bridges and who had responsibility for repairing them. His records refer to the end of the eighteenth century. In some cases the landowner repaired the bridges, in others the parish or both parishes where the river formed the boundary. A few were repaired by the County. When the religious houses owned a good deal of land, the local abbey was responsible for the repair of the bridge, for instance Crawford bridge was repaired by the abbess

at Tarrant Crawford. Until well into the nineteenth century the parishes were responsible for their own roads and shared the responsibility for bridges, but by the twentieth century the County or even the central Government had taken responsibility for both roads and bridges.

Hutchins' records awakened an interest and I soon found Wallis' (1974) account of his work for the Dorset County Council as a bridge engineer. Then I met Sue Clifford of Common Ground, an organisation dedicated to celebrating everything

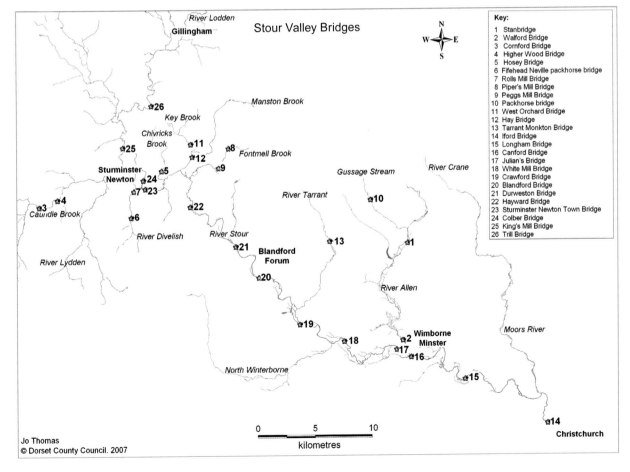

Stour Valley Bridges

Key:
1 Stanbridge
2 Walford Bridge
3 Cornford Bridge
4 Higher Wood Bridge
5 Hosey Bridge
6 Fifehead Neville packhorse bridge
7 Rolls Mill Bridge
8 Piper's Mill Bridge
9 Peggs Mill Bridge
10 Packhorse bridge
11 West Orchard Bridge
12 Hay Bridge
13 Tarrant Monkton Bridge
14 Iford Bridge
15 Longham Bridge
16 Canford Bridge
17 Julian's Bridge
18 White Mill Bridge
19 Crawford Bridge
20 Blandford Bridge
21 Durweston Bridge
22 Hayward Bridge
23 Sturminster Newton Town Bridge
24 Colber Bridge
25 King's Mill Bridge
26 Trill Bridge

Jo Thomas
© Dorset County Council. 2007

0   5   10
kilometres

about the countryside, in Dorset and elsewhere. In 2000 they started on a project about the Stour Valley, and their enthusiasm led me to study the stone bridges in the Stour catchment area. During the summer of 2000 I managed to get reasonably close to all the bridges – cows, nettles, electric fences and so on permitting. However 'close' was often more than 10 feet away. There are, unfortunately, very few footpaths along the river, so I was 'exploring' and cannot suggest that anyone should follow my example.

As I explored, a pattern began to emerge in the use of the stone for the bridges, in which transport of something as heavy as stone seemed to be an important factor. The pattern is dependent on the stone available in each locality as well as on its strength and water resistance. There are many limestones and sandstones used for building houses and churches, but only certain ones will survive standing constantly in water. Within the Stour catchment area they are the Forest Marble limestone and sandstone quarried south of Sherborne, the Upper Greensand sandstone quarried at Shaftesbury, the greenish sandstone from Chilmark in the Vale of Wardour, some of the Tertiary heathstone, and the Purbeck and Portland limestones from the coast.

The Forest Marble and Upper Greensand predominate in the bridges above Blandford, with the ironstone joining the Greensand to the south of the town. Purbeck stone could have been brought up the Stour by sea from the Isle of Purbeck. Many bridges have long histories, but were widened during the late eighteenth century for the turnpikes and repeatedly as transport changed in the nineteenth and twentieth centuries. The stone used has depended on availability at the time.

Sturminster Newton Town Bridge is built of Upper Greensand Shaftesbury Sandstone ashlar. The walls of the mill nearby that stand in the river are also Greensand. Corallian limestone is used for the upper walls of the mill, but it is not suitable for standing in water.

THE BLACKMORE VALE

The waters of the River Stour and its northern tributaries rise from Greensand springs in the Blackmore Vale, where the outcrops of Corallian limestones, much faulted, create a north-south ridge with Oxford and Kimmeridge Clay vales on either side. South of Sturminster Newton the river turns sharply east at the foot of the Chalk scarp and cuts through the Blandford gap where a fault has created a line of weakness in the Chalk. South of Blandford the river is joined by streams draining the south-easterly dip of the Chalk, reaching the Tertiary sands at Sturminster Marshall. Running east-south-east, it joins the Avon and reaches the sea at Christchurch Harbour.

The construction of the older bridges follows the geology but later ones brought stone from further afield. A small bridge in the centre of Gillingham and Trill Bridge in Fifehead Magdalen (ST790205) are built of Upper Greensand from Shaftesbury. King's Mill Bridge near Marnhull (ST766171) was built in 1823 by G.A. Underwood, replacing one of 1673 on the site of one of 1358. The present nineteenth century construction has a Blue Lias parapet, with Bath Stone coping, Bath Stone and Upper Greensand pillars, with Greensand tablets inset. The main structure of the bridge is of small blocks of Forest Marble sandstone. It is probable that the Bath stone was brought on the first part of its journey by rail.

Only a family with a good deal of money could collect together such a variety of stone. A causeway over the floodplain near Lower Farm, Marnhull (ST767201) is built of Forest Marble and several small bridges, such as the supports for Colber Bridge at Sturminster Newton (ST783142), are of small blocks of Forest Marble.

Town Bridge at Sturminster Newton (ST784136) was first built in the sixteenth century of Upper Greensand and widened in the seventeenth century. Widened again in 1820, the northern extension over the flood plain was built in 1828, also of Upper Greensand, but with Forest Marble sandstone under the arches. The workmanship on these small blocks of stone is well worth the trudge across the field. Hayward Bridge in Child Okeford (ST823120) has Upper Greensand piers with iron spans. The tooling on the masonry is similar to Hay Bridge on Manston brook, a much more handsome structure. Durweston Bridge (ST863086) was built in 1795 by Joseph Towsey for H.W. Portman, who closed the original road running through his Bryanston estate and built this bridge and a new road to enter Blandford from the north instead of the south. The whole bridge appears to be of Greensand ashlar, but the original stone on the eastern side is from Chilmark in the Vale of Wardour and the western end on the Durweston side is Upper Greensand from Shaftesbury. In April 2007 the bridge was repaired using new Chilmark Stone. Portman used the stone from Eastbury in Tarrant Gunville to build himself Bryanston House, and probably the stone for the bridges at Durweston and Blandford was from the same source.

THE NORTHERN TRIBUTARIES

Gillingham town bridge (ST807265) is in fact on one of the northern tributaries of the Stour, the Shreen Water. On the River Lodden a bridge on the Shaftesbury road (ST814261) is built of Upper Greensand. Cornford Bridge (ST692120) on Caundle Brook was cleaned and restored in 1994. Dating back to 1480, the main structure is Forest Marble, but there have been many repairs in the eighteenth, nineteenth and twentieth centuries. The stone used for these repairs includes Ham Hill Stone and Sherborne Building Stone. The coping is now mixed, including Ham Hill Stone and some Sherborne Building Stone that can be dated at 1861 by comparison with the same bed of stone used in Bristol Road, Sherborne.

Cornford Bridge on Caundle Brook between Bishop's Caundle and Holwell has foundations of Forest Marble, with many blocks of Ham Hill Stone and some Inferior Oolite from Sherborne.

This bed is in three parts, cream at the top, blue at the bottom, with a thin sliver of broken shell material sandwiched between. The broken shell material was weathering out, and has been rendered over. Some blocks were replaced in 1994 with French stone. During these repairs the cobbled roadway of Forest Marble was uncovered and removed. Higher Wood Bridge (ST708126), also on Caundle Brook, was built in 1770 of Forest Marble. Its rounded cutwaters are continuous with the arches, which is unusual.

On the River Lydden King's Stag Bridge (ST727103) looks very much like Blue Lias, with Ham Hill Stone cutwaters on the upstream side. The three triangular arches are of Ham Hill Stone.

Fifehead Neville packhorse bridge on the River Divelish is built of Forest Marble limestone. The triangular arches are unusual.

The walls of Rolls Mill bridge on the River Divelish close to Sturminster Newton are of Upper Greensand ashlar, but the small blocks under the arches appear to be of Forest Marble.

The base of the pillars appears to be Forest Marble sandstone. Twofords Bridge at Lydlinch was built in the 1830's of Forest Marble, as are the piers of Bagber Bridge.

On the River Divelish the medieval packhorse bridge at Fifehead Neville (ST772111) (*see previous page*) is built of Forest Marble limestone, with two triangular pointed arches made of long blocks of stone that do not appear to be the fan shape one would expect and there is no central keystone. Salkeld Bridge (ST770121) was built in 1857 or 1864, to commemorate Philip Salkeld VC, a hero of the Indian Mutiny. This has Bath stone coping and the parapet is Blue Lias. Rolls Mill Bridge (ST774133) may be eighteenth century, but there are records of repairs in 1689. The piers and parapet are of Upper Greensand ashlar, with rounded cutwaters. Smaller blocks of stone underneath the arch look like the Forest Marble used elsewhere.

On Chivrick's Brook Hosey Bridge (ST799150) is built of Upper Greensand and has a new parapet of Purbeck limestone. On Manston Brook Hay Bridge (ST825162) is a handsome eighteenth or nineteenth century structure of Upper Greensand ashlar. There is a carving on the north side and an inscription and date on the south side said to be the arms of the Grosvenor family. Collyer's Brook rises at Springhead (ST876170), but changes its name to Fontmell Brook in Fontmell Magna at Collyer's Mill Bridge (ST866170). This bridge is brick with Upper Greensand coping and foundations. It has recently been graced with its name elegantly carved into the coping, as part of the Stour Valley Project initiated by Common Ground. Piper's Mill Bridge (ST857169), Peggs Mill Bridge (ST849151) and Farrington Bridge (ST841155), both the latter in Iwerne Minster, are all of Upper Greensand.

SOUTH OF BLANDFORD

Blandford Bridge (ST883060) is in two parts, one over the River Stour, the other over the flood plain. William Moulton built the present structure of Greensand ashlar in 1783, though some medieval ribbed arches of ironstone can be seen under the span at the town end. Judging by the date of construction, the bridge was probably built of stone from Eastbury. In 1812 it was rebuilt and widened again on the downstream side by William Bushrod. Whether the original stone, or new stone, was used is not recorded. When the ground is dry enough to look under the flood plain arches, it is possible to see the three phases of building.

Below Blandford, the next bridge is on the east side of Spetisbury, Crawford Bridge (ST918020), leading to Tarrant Crawford. This was built in 1530 and the upstream side is little altered. It was repaired in 1719 and widened in 1819 on the downstream side, with the date stone of 1719 reset. The main structure upstream is of Greensand and ironstone with a little flint in the walls and arches. Alternate cutwaters are of Greensand ashlar, with ironstone forming a steep-roofed upper part. The other cutwaters are of dressed stone in a mix of Greensand

and ironstone above a foundation of Greensand ashlar, and continue upwards to form refuges. Flint, heathstone and Greensand form a chequer pattern on the downstream side. A bridge is recorded here as early as 1235. Repairs to a northern extension over the flood plain were carried out in August 2000 using Upper Greensand from Shaftesbury excavated when a small bypass was cut into the north side of the hill. At that time the mason reported that the ribs of the arches were of Greensand and the vaulting of flint.

White Mill Bridge (ST957006), between Sturminster Marshall and Shapwick, is the oldest recorded bridge on the Stour. Built in 1174-5, the lower portions are twelfth century, though the arches were rebuilt in the 16th century. The county undertook major repairs in 1713. The whole structure is ironstone, except for alternate pieces of Purbeck Burr in the voussoirs of the arches making an ornamental pattern that can also be seen at Iford and a bridge in Christchurch on the Avon. When repairs were undertaken in the 1960's, the timber rafts supporting the piers on top of 800 year old oak piles were replaced by concrete. Mr. A.J. Wallis, Bridge Engineer for Dorset County Council wrote *A History and Guide to the Dorset Bridges* in 1974. His account of the repairs at White Mill Bridge is an illustration of the care with which such work has been done.

'We started pulling out lengths of old black timber, and then came across the stump ends of old timber piles. The timber was hard and heavy and was in fact oak trunks turned black with lying for centuries in the mud of the river bed. It was similar to the bog

Above Crawford Bridge at Spetisbury has Greensand and flint chequer on the downstream side and cutwaters of heathstone upstream.

Below White Mill bridge between Sturminster Marshall and Shapwick is built of heathstone. The white ornament on the arches is Purbeck Burr limestone.

oak found in Ireland and which can be carved into ornaments.

Apparently the original builders had driven oak piles into the river bed and then built oak rafts on top of them of the size of the required piers. Off these rafts the masonry structure was built. The rafts being nearer the surface of the mud than the piles, had after nearly 800 years started to rot and let the edge stones of the piers sink. The tops of the piles were slightly affected, but once these were scraped the rest were in perfect condition due to the depth of mud excluding all oxygen, as is the case with old hulks preserved in the sea bed.

So in short lengths at a time all the rotted timber

was pulled out and scraped away and all sunk and dislodged stonework was removed and then concrete was inserted to replace the timber raft. The stonework was then made good, and the work continued round all seven piers and the two abutments.'

Julian's Bridge (SZ002998), on the Corfe Mullen side of Wimborne, has ironstone underneath the arches, set back from the present bridge walls. This ironstone is part of the bridge built in 1636 to replace the late fifteenth century bridge named after Walter Julien of Wimborne who lived during King John's reign. It was repaired in 1713 and widened both sides in 1836 and 1844 with an additional arch at the eastern end. When it was widened to 18 feet between the parapets, pointed brick arches with stone dressings of Greensand and Purbeck were built over the cutwaters, framing the earlier spans. It therefore appears to be a stone bridge with a string course of Purbeck stone topped by a brick parapet with stone coping. The three flood arches on the Corfe Mullen side were built in brick, with Portland stone dressing.

Canford Bridge (SZ016993), on the Merley side of Wimborne, was built in 1813 by John Dyson engineer and Jesse Bushrod mason (see Blandford). The walls are of Purbeck Freestone ashlar, with Portland Roach piers. The viaduct on the southern end is built of ironstone and Purbeck limestone (some Burr) in the arches, piers and cutwaters, with some Greensand. Purbeck limestone blocks top the stone part with typical nineteenth century tooling.

Longham Bridge (SZ064973) is recorded as being built by John Wagg of Ringwood in 1728, and the upstream arches are of ironstone ashlar underneath. The cutwaters are of Greensand, which is more easily visible on the downstream side. The last stone bridge over the Stour is at Iford (SZ138935), where two separate bridges cross the two parts of the river.

Top Canford Bridge at Wimborne has Portland Freestone Roach piers and Purbeck Freestone walls.

Upper Middle Iford Bridge was built of Purbeck limestone in the eighteenth century.

Lower Middle The packhorse bridge at Tarrant Monkton is built of greensand, with two large sarsens standing at the edge of the water.

Bottom On the River Allen there has been a stone bridge (Stanbridge) near the Horton Inn for centuries. The present bridge is mostly Greensand but where it has been widened the voussoirs are of Purbeck Freestone.

Although a stone bridge is recorded in the twelfth century, none of this remains. The oldest bridge now standing spans the eastern stream and was built in the mid seventeenth century of Purbeck Burr, ironstone (possibly from Hengistbury Head) and other Purbeck limestones in small blocks. An ironstone/Purbeck stone pattern can be seen on the voussoirs, as at White Mill. In the main bridge, over the western stream, the first two arches were built in 1784 of Purbeck Burr ashlar, designed by Robert Mylne, who also designed the original Blackfriars Bridge in London. In 1933 two matching arches were built at the eastern end of the eighteenth century spans.

THE SOUTHERN TRIBUTARIES

Below Blandford the southern tributaries of the Stour include the Pimperne, which has no stone bridges. The River Tarrant rises from springs in the road at Stubhampton upstream of Tarrant Gunville. The first bridge is by the gateway to Eastbury House (ST927126), where the gateway and bridge show both types of Greensand, the Upper Greensand from Shaftesbury and the sandstone from Chilmark that appears to be finer grained and to resist weathering better. At Tarrant Monkton the medieval packhorse bridge (ST945090) still stands by the ford and is protected at each end by sarsen stones from the Tertiary sands. The sands have been weathered away from the Chalk in this valley, but there are a few sarsens remaining. The other Tarrant bridges are of brick or concrete.

The North Winterborne rises at Winterborne Stickland but the first bridges of stone are at Winterborne Kingston (SY862977), being rockfaced Purbeck of typical 19th century masonry. The packhorse bridge in Sturminster Marshall (SU946001) described as 17th century is mostly of ironstone.

Over the mill stream at Didlington (*above*) is an elegant bridge built of Chilmark stone, but over the River Allen itself (*below*) the arches of the bridge are of Chilmark stone, with the parapet walls of brick.

The bridge at Stanbridge Mill (SU013089) is the northernmost stone bridge on the River Allen. In 1279 *Pons Petrae* (the stone bridge) marked the outer limits of Cranborne Chase. In 1760 the bridge was widened to take the turnpike road from Ringwood to Shaftesbury and the structure now seen is built of Greensand and Purbeck Freestone. Earlier arches can be clearly seen underneath. Hidden in the woods to the south are two bridges, one over the Allen at Didlington (SU007082), built of Chilmark stone with a brick parapet, and one over the Didlington mill stream (SU007079). The second is a most elegant bridge entirely of Chilmark stone in the style of Vanbrugh. Walford Bridge (SU009006) on the northern edge of Wimborne was a medieval packhorse bridge built of ironstone. The upstream side can be seen from the pub car park and shows seventeenth century work, but the downstream side that was remodelled in 1802 is obscured by a footway.

CHAPTER ELEVEN

Brickmaking

A detailed study of the use of clays would not be appropriate for this volume, but I have found evidence, either in surviving historic buildings or on Ordnance Survey maps showing brickworks, that every clay found in Dorset has been used for brickmaking at some time in the past.

A few houses built in the seventeenth century would have used kilns on their own land that have completely disappeared, but there are records and some remains of eighteenth century kilns. The fires caused by thatch roofs in several towns at the end of the seventeenth and beginning of the eighteenth century have resulted in eighteenth century brick townscapes of great character. Although few kilns remain, the names of fields on tithe maps give the best clue to their presence. Mechanisation of brickmaking during the nineteenth century gave the opportunity for towns to expand rapidly and many of the brickworks have been recorded in John Lowe's 'Dorset Building Materials Survey. A Pilot Project. March 1994'.

To illustrate the use of clays, it will be logical to take the areas previously described – the Marshwood Vale and near Bridport, the Blackmore Vale, the Weymouth area and the East Dorset heathlands.

MARSHWOOD VALE

The Lower and Middle Lias clays are available in the Marshwood Vale, and have been used for cob as well as brickmaking. Close to Bridport the Upper Lias Down Cliff Clay has been used.

Bettiscombe Manor is outwardly a brick house, though it has an older core inside. The brickwork was undertaken in three stages, commencing in 1694, using a different size brick in each stage. Owned by the Pinney family for centuries, the eighteenth century improvement was built for John Pinney, rector of Broadwindsor, probably with funds from the family's West Indies sugar plantations. The mottled grey and yellow clay on which the Manor stands is an ancient landslip from Sliding Hill. The bricks were made from this slipped mixture of Eype Clay and other Middle Lias silts in a small kiln which can still be seen in a nearby field. Extra clay was brought from another pit south of the stream, where the Green Ammonite Beds are still in situ. The bricks were laid in a distinctive chequerboard pattern of vitrified headers and deep red stretchers. Bricks from this kiln were also used for a lace factory in Lyme Regis and some cottages in Whitchurch Canonicorum. Racedown House was also built for the Pinney family, in 1785, from John Pretor's kilns not far from the house.

The tithe map for Netherbury and Isaac Taylor's map of 1770 show field names like Brickpit Moors, and Brick Field showing that bricks were made there during the eighteenth century of Middle Lias clays.

The earliest indication of The Marshwood Brick and Tile Works is on an estate map of John Tatchell Bullen in 1852, where 'Bricky"d' is pencilled in. This factory used the Belemnite Marls, and the records show that the factory was working between the 1880's and 1904.

The North Allington brickworks, whose buildings can still be seen, used Down Cliff Clay from the north side of Allington Hill and the east side of Coneygar Hill. Various pits were being worked between 1785 and 1890 and have been noted in Kelly's Directories as well as in the geological Memoir.

EAST OF BRIDPORT

When the railway was being built towards West Bay in 1857 kilns were built on Powerstock Common using the Fuller's Earth Clay to provide bricks for the bridges required to carry the railway. The yellow bricks were also used in Bridport between 1858 and 1865. These kilns can

Bettiscombe Manor was clad in brick during the 18th century using Green Ammonite Bed and Middle Lias clay from its own fields made in its own kiln.

still be seen at SY542974 in the nature reserve.

At Bothenhampton the complicated faulting brings a small outcrop of Oxford Clay to the surface in the land belonging to the Gundry family. This was used for brickmaking at SY483913 from 1889 until 1952. The quality of the clay that could be won from the pit had deteriorated because the remaining beds contained too much fossil shell. The site has been used as a rubbish tip and is now restored to grassland.

BLACKMORE VALE

The Oxford and Kimmeridge Clays were available for brickmaking on the west and east side respectively of the Corallian limestone ridge that runs from Marnhull southwards to Sturminster Newton. The Gault Clay was also used in areas close to the Cretaceous Chalk downland.

In the Blackmore Vale Gillingham and Blandford both suffered disastrous fires, in 1694 and 1731 respectively. The towns were rebuilt in brick and although brickyards from this date do not survive, the names of fields given on tithe maps can indicate where they were. The 1841 tithe map for Gillingham shows 'brickyard' at ST817262 and 'Brickhills

Ground' at ST825249. Both of these are on the Kimmeridge Clay. Nineteenth century brickyards operated at ST808259 and ST818262, also on the Kimmeridge Clay, the first being the Gillingham Brick and Tile Co., working between 1866 and 1969.

The town of Blandford Forum was not so well placed for brickmaking clay, but the tithe map for Blandford St. Mary shows Brickkiln Field on the valley alluvium. However, the Bryanston Estate had a brickyard on the Clay with Flints at Folly (ST842082) which was working in both the eighteenth and nineteenth centuries. It is possible that bricks were brought to Blandford from Child Okeford where bricks were made for Fontmell Parva House and later at Gold Hill (ST830135) from the Kimmeridge Clay. Bricks were made from the Gault at Iwerne Courtney (ST844141) from 1838 to 1886 and from 1838 to 1911 at the Iwerne Minster brickworks (ST848150). It is possible that bricks were being made earlier in the same areas and could have been used for the eighteenth century rebuilding of Blandford.

Other brickworks recorded in the Blackmore Vale included Hawker's Hill, Motcombe, for the

Above The upper storeys of the Red Lion Inn and its neighbours remain as originally built after the fire of 1731.

Below Old Bank House next to St. Peter's church in Blandford was built after the 1731 fire using clay from the upper Stour valley. Both Kimmeridge Clay and Gault Clay were used in different brickyards.

Grosvenor Estate (ST85202385) working from 1858 to 1939, using Kimmeridge Clay. The Marnhull brick and tile works (ST775202) originally owned by John Hussey, used Oxford Clay from 1850 to 1901. The main brickworks near Sturminster Newton were those at Bagber (ST755131) using Oxford Clay, working from 1842 to 1911. Other brick and tile works in the Oxford Clay were at Ryme Intrinseca, Evershot, Kings Stag and Holnest. At Okeford Fitzpaine the brickworks using Gault clay at ST814108 were still visible until near the end of the twentieth century, having closed in 1939.

THE WEYMOUTH AREA

West of Weymouth, in Chickerell, there were several brickworks in the Oxford Clay, the best known being Crookhill (SY644797) and Putton Lane (SY650798). These both seem to have been working in the late nineteenth century and into the twentieth century. Putton Lane closed in the late 1960's and Crookhill in the early 1970's. Those who remember the brickworks say that they ran out of good clay. However, in their time they provided considerable quantities of bricks for Weymouth.

SOUTH AND EAST DORSET

East of Weymouth, the Chalk hills are soon covered by Tertiary beds and the earliest Palaeogene Reading Beds were used at Broadmayne, Coombe Keynes and Bere Regis. There were five sites in Broadmayne working from the eighteenth century to 1939, of which Watergate Lane (SY731871) was the earliest. Broadmayne brick was used extensively in Dorchester and can easily be recognised by the black spots in red purple-brown bricks. These black spots are the result of specks of manganese. The earliest building in Dorchester using Broadmayne bricks is 52 High West Street, built in the first quarter of the eighteenth century. 6 High East street and 3 Trinity Street are only slightly later.

The Weld Estate brickyard and tilery at Coombe Keynes (SY840843) produced red and brown bricks.

Broadmayne brick in Dorchester.

At Bere Regis the Drax estate brickyards at Doddings (SY854936), working from the eighteenth century to 1911, produced red, orange and blue tinted bricks that can be seen in the south wall and porch of the church. There were other brickyards at Hundred Barrow (SY842938) and Hollow Oak (SY848938). The cottages on the main street are all of the local brick, but unfortunately many have now been painted and thus lost their local character. The Drax estate wall at Charborough Park used Doddings bricks. The earliest record of the use of Bere Regis bricks is for Anderson Manor in 1622 where two stretcher courses of delicate pinks were built with one header course of deep purple (flared).

Clay from the Wareham area in the Poole Formation has proved to be of a very high quality and has been used for domestic pottery, for sanitary ware, for imparting a sheen to paper, for tiles, but not so much for bricks. The brickmaking area includes Creekmoor, Corfe Mullen and the whole Poole and Bournemouth conurbation. A good deal of the clay was used for drainage pipes throughout this area, but the towns grew rapidly in the nineteenth century using locally made bricks. The clays used in Corfe Mullen were from the London Clay, but across from Lytchett Minster (12 brickworks) and Creekmoor (6) to Bournemouth they were in the Poole Formation and Branksome Sand. They have been given the names of the areas where they reached the surface – Creekmoor, Oakdale, Broadstone and Parkstone. Within the Borough of Poole there were 55 brickyards. The clay from the Branksome Sand was used in the Bournemouth brickworks, of which 21 are recorded. Two brickyards opened on Brownsea Island in the Parkstone Clay, but the clay here was so poor that the bricks are disintegrating and the beach near the old brickworks now consists entirely of broken shards of pipe. As these clays were deposited by a river, the quality of each clay was different and even where it has the same name, being at the same level in the series, it can differ in organic or sand content.

There were small brickyards near Wimborne using

Top Horton Tower is a folly built as an observatory during the 19th century with bricks made in a nearby field of Reading Beds clay.

Bottom The mill at Corfe Mullen, of bricks made a hundred metres away in Brickyard Lane of London Clay used in the 20th century for Poole tiles.

West End House is an eighteenth century merchant's house in St. James Place, Poole, built of local brick made from Poole Formation clay. Each of the clays in this series has different organic or mineral content, which produces different colour bricks.

London Clay at Knobcrook (SU007007) and either London Clay or Poole Formation at 3 yards in Colehill. These were owned by the Bankes Estate, and are now on National Trust land, though none are still working. At Wimborne St. Giles Sutton Holms brickyard, owned by the Earl of Shaftesbury, used London Clay but closed on the eve of the first World War.

Verwood is famous for its potteries, but there were also brickworks in the London Clay at Manor Brickworks, Black Hill at SU095087. Many of the small pottery kilns can still be seen, preserved as a feature in gardens.

SWANAGE

Standing alone at Godlingston is the one remaining brickyard in Dorset, using Wealden clay for hand-made bricks. Continuing in work from 1700 to the present day, it can be found at SZ020803.

Brick Clays in Dorset
showing stratigraphic sequence
Not to scale

	Clay	Building Stone
Quaternary	Clay with flints	Flint
Tertiary: Eocene	Branksome Sand clay	
	Poole Formation:	
	Parkstone	
	Broadstone	Heathstone
	Oakdale	
	Creekmoor	
Tertiary: Palaeocene	London Clay	Lytchett Matravers Sand
		Warmwell Farm Sand
	Reading Beds	
Cretaceous		Chalk
		Upper Greensand
	Gault	
	Wealden clay	
		Purbeck limestone
Jurassic		Portland limestone
	Kimmeridge Clay	
		Corallian limestone
	Oxford Clay	
		Forest Marble
	Fuller's Earth Clay	
		Inferior Oolite
	Down Cliff Clay	
		Junction Bed
	Eype Clay	
	Green Ammonite Beds	
	Belemnite Marls	
		Blue Lias

CHAPTER TWELVE

Building Stone by Parish

Parish	NGR	Stone 1	Stone 2	Stone 3	Stone 4	Stone 5	Other 1	Other 2
ABBOTSBURY	SY5785	Corallian	Lower Purbeck	Portland				
AFFPUDDLE	SY8093	Portland	Lower Purbeck	Heathstone	Flint		Cob	Brick
ALDERHOLT	SU1112	Heathstone	Purbeck				Cob	Brick
ALLINGTON	SY4693	Inferior Oolite	Forest Marble				Brick	
ALMER	SY9198	Flint	Lytchett Matravers Sandstone	Purbeck	Greensand		Cob	
ALTON PANCRAS	ST6902	Flint	Lower Purbeck				Cob	Brick
ANDERSON	SY8897	Heathstone	Ham Hill Stone	Portland	Flint		Brick	
ARNE	SY9788	Purbeck	Poole Formation heathstone				Brick	Cob
ASHMORE	ST9117	Upper Greensand	Flint				Brick	
ASKERSWELL	SY5292	Inferior Oolite						
ATHELHAMPTON	SY7794	Lower Purbeck	Portland	Bath stone				
BATCOMBE	ST6104	Chalk	Upper Greensand	Flint				
BEAMINSTER	ST4701	Inferior Oolite	Ham Hill Stone	Flint			Brick	Cob
BEER HACKETT	ST6011	Inferior Oolite	Fuller's Earth Rock	Forest Marble				
BENVILLE	ST5403	Forest Marble	Flint					
BERE REGIS	SY8494	Flint	Purbeck	Heathstone	Ham Hill Stone		Brick	
BETTISCOMBE	SY3999	Inferior Oolite	Upper Greensand chert	Blue Lias			Brick	
BINCOMBE	SY6884	Lower Purbeck	Cornbrash					
BINDON ABBEY	SY8586	Heathstone	Flint				Cob	
BISHOPS CAUNDLE	ST6913	Forest Marble	Cornbrash	Corallian			Cob	
BLACKDOWN	ST3903	Upper Greensand chert						
BLANDFORD	ST8906	Portland	Upper Greensand	Chalk			Brick	
BLANDFORD ST. MARY	ST8805	Flint	Heathstone				Brick	Cob
BLOXWORTH	SY8794	Purbeck	Flint				Brick	Cob
BOCKHAMPTON	SZ1796	Heathstone						
L. BOCKHAMPTON	SY7290	Purbeck						

Parish	NGR	Stone 1	Stone 2	Stone 3	Stone 4	Stone 5	Other 1	Other 2
BOTHENHAMPTON	SY4791	Forest Marble						
BOURNEMOUTH	SZ0891	Purbeck	Bath stone				Brick	
BOURTON	ST7730	Upper Greensand	Corallian				Brick	
BOWDEN	ST7723	Forest Marble						
BRADFORD ABBAS	ST5814	Inferior Oolite	Ham Hill Stone					
BRADFORD PEVERELL	SY6593	Flint	Lower Purbeck				Cob	
BRADPOLE	SY4794	Inferior Oolite	Forest Marble				Cob	
BRIDPORT	SY4692	Forest Marble	Inferior Oolite	Ham Hill Stone			Brick	
BROADMAYNE	SY7286	Lower Purbeck	Portland				Brick	
BROADOAK	SY4396	Inferior Oolite						
BROADWEY	SY6683	Lower Purbeck						
BROADWINDSOR	ST4302	Inferior Oolite	Ham Hill Stone					
BROWNSEA ISLAND	SZ0187	Purbeck					Brick	
BRYANSTON	ST8707	Tisbury sandstone					Brick	Cob
BRYANTSPUDDLE	SY8191						Brick	Cob
BUCKHORN WESTON	ST7524	Corallian					Brick	
BUCKLAND NEWTON	ST6805	Upper Greensand	Ham Hill Stone				Brick	Cob
BUCKLAND RIPERS	SY6582	Corallian						
BURSTOCK	ST4202	Inferior Oolite						
BURTON BRADSTOCK	SY4889	Forest Marble	Inferior Oolite				Brick	Cob
CANFORD MAGNA	SZ0398	Poole Formation heathstone	Purbeck					
CANN	ST8721	Upper Greensand	Corallian				Brick	
CATHERSTON LEWESTON	SY3794	Upper Greensand chert	Inferior Oolite	Ham Hill Stone				
CATTISTOCK	SY5999	Chalk	Flint	Forest Marble	Ham Hill Stone		Brick	Cob
CAUNDLE MARSH	ST6713	Forest Marble	Cornbrash	Inferior Oolite				
CERNE ABBAS	ST6601	Chalk	Lower Purbeck	Flint	Portland	Ham Hill Stone	Brick	Cob
CHALBURY	SU0106	Upper Greensand	Tisbury sandstone	Heathstone			Brick	
CHALDON HERRING	SY7983	Lower Purbeck	Portland	Flint	Heathstone	Burr	Brick	
CHALMINGTON	ST5900	Chalk	Flint					
CHARBOROUGH PARK	SY9297	Purbeck	Heathstone				Brick	

Parish	NGR	Stone 1	Stone 2	Stone 3	Stone 4	Stone 5	Other 1	Other 2
CHARLTON MARSHALL	SZ9003	Upper Greensand	Flint				Brick	Cob
CHARMINSTER	SY6792	Lower Purbeck	Chalk	Flint			Brick	Cob
CHARMOUTH	SY3693	Upper Greensand chert	Inferior Oolite	Blue Lias	Forest Marble		Brick	
CHEDINGTON	ST4805	Inferior Oolite	Upper Greensand					
CHELBOROUGH	ST5505	Forest Marble	Chalk	Flint				
CHETNOLE	ST6008	Forest Marble	Cornbrash				Brick	
CHETTLE	ST9513	Flint	Upper Greensand	Tisbury sandstone			Brick	
CHICKERELL	SY6480	Lower Purbeck	Forest Marble	Cornbrash	Corallian	Portland	Brick	Cob
CHIDEOCK	SY4292	Inferior Oolite	Upper Greensand chert	Blue Lias			Cob	
CHILD OKEFORD	ST8312	Corallian	Upper Greensand	Chalk	Flint		Brick	Cob
CHILFROME	SY5898	Flint	Chalk	Upper Greensand			Brick	Cob
CHRISTCHURCH	SZ1692	Purbeck	Hengistbury ironstone	Portland	Quarr from I.o.Wight	Barton Bed G	Brick	
CHURCH KNOWLE	SY9481	Purbeck						
CLIFTON MAYBANK	ST5713	Inferior Oolite	Ham Hill Stone				Brick	
COLEHILL	SU0200	Heathstone					Brick	Cob
COMPTON ABBAS	ST8718	Upper Greensand						
COMPTON VALENCE	SY5993	Upper Greensand	Portland	Chalk	Flint	Ham Hill Stone	Cob	
COOMBE KEYNES	SY8484	Heathstone	Purbeck	Flint			Brick	
CORFE CASTLE	SY9682	Purbeck	Flint	Heathstone			Brick	Cob
CORFE MULLEN	SY9798	Poole Formation heathstone	Purbeck	Bath stone			Timber frame	
CORSCOMBE	ST5105	Forest Marble	Cornbrash	Flint	Chalk			
TOLLER WHELME	ST5101	Upper Greensand	Flint	Inferior Oolite				
CRANBORNE	SU0514	Heathstone	Flint	Upper Greensand	Tisbury sandstone		Cob	Brick
CRICHEL, MOOR	ST9908	Portland					Cob	
CRICHEL, LONG	ST9710	Upper Greensand	Tisbury sandstone	Flint	Portland		Brick	
DEWLISH	ST7797	Lower Purbeck	Portland	Ham Hill Stone				
DORCHESTER	SY6890	Lower Purbeck	Portland	Flint	Bath stone		Brick	
DURWESTON	ST8508	Flint	Corallian	Upper Greensand	Tisbury sandstone		Brick	Cob
EAST ORCHARD	ST8317	Upper Greensand	Corallian				Brick	
EAST STOKE	SY8786	Purbeck	Poole Formation heathstone				Brick	Cob
EAST STOUR	ST7922	Corallian						

Parish	NGR	Stone 1	Stone 2	Stone 3	Stone 4	Stone 5	Other 1	Other 2
EDMONDSHAM	SU0611	Heathstone	Flint	Upper Greensand	Tisbury sandstone		Brick	Cob
EVERSHOT	ST5704	Forest Marble	Flint	Chalk			Brick	
FARNHAM	ST9515	Flint	Upper Greensand	Tisbury sandstone			Brick	Cob
FIDDLEFORD	ST8013	Corallian	Upper Greensand	Ham Hill Stone				
FIFEHEAD MAGDALEN	ST7821	Corallian	Upper Greensand	Forest Marble				
FIFEHEAD NEVILLE	ST7610	Corallian	Forest Marble				Brick	Cob
FLEET	SY6380	Forest Marble	Cornbrash	Portland			Cob	
FOLKE	ST6513	Forest Marble	Cornbrash	Ham Hill Stone			Brick	
FONTMELL MAGNA	ST8616	Upper Greensand	Flint	Corallian	Chalk		Brick	Timber frame
FORDE ABBEY	ST3505	Upper Greensand chert	Upper Greensand grit	Ham Hill Stone				
FRAMPTON	SY6295	Flint	Portland	Ham Hill Stone	Chalk	Purbeck Marble	Brick	
FROME ST. QUINTIN	ST5902	Flint	Chalk	Upper Greensand			Brick	
FROME VAUCHURCH	SY5996	Flint	Upper Greensand					
GILLINGHAM	ST8026	Corallian	Upper Greensand				Brick	
GLANVILLES WOOTTON	ST6708	Forest Marble	Cornbrash				Cob	Brick
GOATHILL	ST6717	Inferior Oolite	Forest Marble					
GODMANSTONE	SY6697	Flint	Lower Purbeck	Chalk			Cob	Brick
GUSSAGE ALL SAINTS	SU0010	Flint	Heathstone	Upper Greensand	Tisbury sandstone	Bath Stone	Brick	Timber frame
GUSSAGE ST. MICHAEL	ST9811	Flint	Upper Greensand	Heathstone	Tisbury sandstone	Bath Stone	Brick	
GUY'S MARSH	ST8420	Corallian	Upper Greensand					
HALSTOCK	ST5307	Forest Marble	Cornbrash					
HAMMOON	ST8114	Corallian	Upper Greensand	Forest Marble				
HAMPRESTON	SZ0598	Heathstone	Upper Greensand				Brick	Cob
HANFORD	ST8410	Corallian	Upper Greensand	Bath stone			Brick	
HAYDON	ST6715	Forest Marble						
HAZELBURY BRYAN	ST7408	Corallian					Brick	Cob
HERMITAGE	ST6407	Forest Marble	Flint	Corallian	Upper Greensand	Upper Greensand chert		
HILFIELD	ST6304	Forest Marble	Flint	Upper Greensand	Chalk	Upper Greensand chert	Brick	

Parish	NGR	Stone 1	Stone 2	Stone 3	Stone 4	Stone 5	Other 1	Other 2
HILTON	ST7802	Flint	Ham Hill Stone	?limestone			Brick	
HINTON MARTELL	SU0106	Flint	Heathstone	Purbeck	Upper Greensand	Bath Stone	Brick	Cob
HINTON PARVA	SU0004	Purbeck	Portland	Flint	Tisbury sandstone	Bath Stone	Brick	
HINTON ST. MARY	ST7816	Corallian	Upper Greensand				Brick	Timber frame
HOLDENHURST	SZ1295	Purbeck	Heathstone				Brick	
HOLME, EAST	SY9085	Purbeck	Heathstone				Brick	
HOLNEST	ST6509	Forest Marble					Brick	
HOLT	SU0203	Heathstone	Bath Stone				Brick	Cob
HOLWELL	ST6911	Cornbrash	Forest Marble	Ham Hill Stone	Inferior Oolite		Brick	
HOOKE	ST5300	Chalk	Inferior Oolite	Ham Hill Stone				
HORTON	SU0307	Upper Greensand	Heathstone	Tisbury sandstone	Flint	Purbeck	Brick	Cob
IWERNE COURTNEY	ST8512	Upper Greensand	Flint	Chalk	Corallian		Brick	Cob
IWERNE MINSTER	ST8614	Upper Greensand	Flint	Corallian	Tisbury sandstone		Brick	
IWERNE STEPLETON	ST8611	Corallian	Upper Greensand	Flint	Chalk		Brick	
KIMMERIDGE	SY9179	Purbeck	Kimmeridge Clay cementstone					
KINGSTON	SY9579	Purbeck						
KINGSTON MAURWARD	SY7191	Portland					Brick	
KINGSTON RUSSELL	SY5789	Portland	Flint	Chalk	Corallian	Purbeck	Forest Marble	
KINGTON MAGNA	ST7623	Corallian	Upper Greensand	Ham Hill Stone				
KINSON	SZ0696	Poole Formation heathstone	Purbeck					
KNOWLTON	SU0210	Flint	Heathstone	Upper Greensand	Tisbury sandstone			
LANGTON HERRING	SY6182	Forest Marble	Corallian	Cornbrash				
LANGTON MATRAVERS	SY9978	Purbeck						
LEIGH	ST6108	Forest Marble	Cornbrash					
LEWESTON	ST6312	Forest Marble	Inferior Oolite	Ham Hill Stone			Brick	
LILLINGTON	ST6212	Forest Marble	Inferior Oolite					
LITTLE BREDY	SY5889	Purbeck	Corallian	Caen	Flint		Brick	Cob
LITTON CHENEY	SY5590	Forest Marble	Corallian	Chalk				
LODERS	SY4994	Inferior Oolite	Forest Marble					Cob

Parish	NGR	Stone 1	Stone 2	Stone 3	Stone 4	Stone 5	Other 1	Other 2
LONG BREDY	SY5891	Forest Marble	Purbeck	Portland	Corallian	Chalk	Flint	Ham Hill
LONG BURTON	ST6412	Forest Marble	Ham Hill Stone					
LULWORTH, EAST	SY8682	Purbeck	Flint	Heathstone	Portland	Chalk	Brick	
LULWORTH, WEST	SY8280	Purbeck						
LYDLINCH	ST7413	Corallian					Brick	Cob
LYME REGIS	SY3492	Blue Lias	Upper Greensand	Portland			Brick	
LYTCHETT MATRAVERS	SY9396	Lytchett Matravers Sandstone	Purbeck	Bath stone			Brick	
LYTCHETT MINSTER	SY9693	Lytchett Matravers Sandstone	Purbeck				Brick	Cob
MAIDEN NEWTON	SY5997	Flint	Chalk	Purbeck	Ham Hill Stone		Brick	
MANGERTON	SY4895	Inferior Oolite						
MANSTON	ST8115	Corallian	Upper Greensand				Brick	
MAPPERTON	SY5099	Inferior Oolite	Ham Hill Stone					
MAPPOWDER	ST7306	Corallian	Upper Greensand					
MARGARET MARSH	ST8213	Corallian						
MARNHULL	ST7718	Corallian	Upper Greensand					
MARSHWOOD	SY3899	Upper Greensand chert	Blue Lias				Brick	Cob
MELBURY ABBAS	ST8820	Upper Greensand Shaftesbury Sandstone	Corallian	Melbury sandstone				
MELBURY BUBB	ST5906	Forest Marble						
MELBURY OSMOND	ST5707	Forest Marble	Ham Hill Stone					Cob
MELBURY SAMPFORD	ST5705	Ham Hill Stone	Forest Marble	Portland			Brick	
MELCOMBE HORSEY	ST7702	Corallian	Flint	Purbeck			Brick	
MELPLASH	SY4898	Inferior Oolite	Junction Bed					
MILTON ABBAS	ST7902	Corallian	Tisbury sandstone	Chalk	Ham Hill Stone	Upper Greensand	Purbeck	Portland
MINTERNE MAGNA	ST6504	Upper Greensand	Flint	Forest Marble	Ham Hill Stone			
MORDEN	SY9195	Heathstone	Ham Hill Stone	Tisbury sandstone			Brick	Cob
MORETON	SY8089	Purbeck					Brick	Cob
MOSTERTON	ST4505	Inferior Oolite	Upper Greensand chert					
MOTCOMBE	ST8525	Upper Greensand	Bath Stone				Brick	
NETHERBURY	SY4799	Inferior Oolite	Junction Bed					Cob
NETHER CERNE	SY6798	Flint	Purbeck				Brick	

Parish	NGR	Stone 1	Stone 2	Stone 3	Stone 4	Stone 5	Other 1	Other 2
NETHER COMPTON	ST5917	Inferior Oolite	Junction Bed	Ham Hill Stone				
NORTH POORTON	SY5198	Inferior Oolite	Bath Stone					
NORTH WOOTTON	ST6514	Forest Marble	Cornbrash					
NOTTINGTON	SY6682	Forest Marble						
OBORNE	ST6518	Inferior Oolite	Ham Hill Stone					
OKEFORD FITZPAINE	ST8010	Upper Greensand	Corallian	Flint	Heathstone		Brick	Cob
OSMINGTON	SY7282	Portland						Cob
OVER COMPTON	ST5916	Inferior Oolite	Ham Hill Stone					
OWERMOIGNE	SY7685	Portland	Purbeck				Brick	Cob
PAMPHILL	ST9900	Purbeck	Heathstone				Brick	Cob
PENTRIDGE	SU0317	Flint					Brick	Cob
PIDDLEHINTON	SY7197	Flint	Purbeck	Ham Hill Stone			Brick	
PIDDLETRENTHIDE	SY7099	Flint	Purbeck	Ham Hill Stone			Brick	Cob
PILSDON	SY4199	Inferior Oolite						
PIMPERNE	SZ9009	Flint					Brick	Cob
POOLE	SZ0191	Purbeck	Poole Formation heathstone	Bath stone			Brick	
PORTESHAM	SY6085	Portland	Purbeck	Corallian	Bath stone			
PORTLAND	SY6872	Portland						
POWERSTOCK	SY5196	Inferior Oolite						
POXWELL	SY7484	Portland	Purbeck				Brick	
POYNTINGTON	ST6419	Inferior Oolite	Ham Hill Stone					
PUDDLETOWN	SY7594	Purbeck	Flint	Upper Greensand			Brick	Cob
PULHAM	ST7008	Cornbrash					Brick	Cob
PUNCKNOWLE	SY5388	Forest Marble	Cornbrash					Cob
PURSE CAUNDLE	ST6917	Fuller's Earth Rock	Inferior Oolite	Forest Marble	Corallian			
RADIPOLE	SY6681	Forest Marble	Cornbrash	Purbeck	Ham Hill Stone			
RAMPISHAM	ST5602	Flint	Chalk	Forest Marble	Cornbrash	Ham Hill Stone	Brick	Cob
RYME INTRINSECA	ST5810	Cornbrash	Forest Marble					
SANDFORD ORCAS	ST6221	Inferior Oolite	White Lias	Junction Bed	Doulting, Inferior Oolite	Ham Hill Stone		
SEABOROUGH	ST4206	Inferior Oolite	Upper Greensand chert					
SHAFTESBURY	ST8622	Upper Greensand	Corallian	Bath stone	Tisbury sandstone		Brick	
SHAPWICK	ST9301	Heathstone	Flint	Purbeck	Upper Greensand	Ham Hill Stone	Brick	Cob

Parish	NGR	Stone 1	Stone 2	Stone 3	Stone 4	Stone 5	Other 1	Other 2
SHERBORNE	ST6313	Inferior Oolite	Ham Hill Stone	Forest Marble	Fuller's Earth Rock			
SHILLINGSTONE	ST8211	Corallian	Upper Greensand	Flint			Brick	
SHIPTON GORGE	SY4991	Inferior Oolite	Forest Marble	Ham Hill Stone				
SILTON	ST7829	Corallian	Upper Greensand					
SIXPENNY HANDLEY	ST9917	Flint	Upper Greensand	Tisbury sandstone			Brick	Cob
SOUTH PERROTT	ST4706	Inferior Oolite						
SPETISBURY	ST9102	Flint	Heathstone	Upper Greensand			Brick	Cob
ST. LEONARDS & ST.IVES	SU1304	Heathstone	Purbeck	Chimark limestone			Brick	
STALBRIDGE	ST7317	Forest Marble	Cornbrash	Corallian				Cob
STANTON ST. GABRIEL	SY4092	Upper Greensand chert	Blue Lias	Beer	Salcombe Regis sst.		Brick	
STEEPLE	SY9181	Purbeck						
STINSFORD	SY7191	Purbeck	Portland	Flint	Ham Hill Stone		Brick	Cob
STOCKWOOD	ST5806	Forest Marble	Ham Hill Stone	Flint			Brick	
STOKE ABBOTT	ST4500	Inferior Oolite						
STOKE WAKE	ST7606						Brick	
STOURPAINE	ST8609	Flint	Upper Greensand	Corallian			Brick	Cob
STOUR PROVOST	ST7921	Corallian						
STOURTON CAUNDLE	ST7013	Forest Marble	Upper Greensand					
STRATTON	SY6593	Flint	Purbeck	Ham Hill Stone				Cob
STUDLAND	SZ0382	Purbeck	Poole Formation heathstone					
STURMINSTER MARSHALL	ST9500	Heathstone	Upper Greensand	Purbeck	Flint		Brick	Cob
STURMINSTER NEWTON	ST7814	Corallian	Upper Greensand	Ham Hill Stone			Brick	Cob
SUTTON POYNTZ	SY7083	Purbeck						
SUTTON WALDRON	ST8816	Upper Greensand	Flint	Corallian			Brick	
SWANAGE	SZ0278	Purbeck						
SWYRE	SY5288	Forest Marble						
SYDLING ST. NICHOLAS	SY6399	Flint	Chalk				Brick	Cob
SYMONDSBURY	SY4493	Inferior Oolite	Forest Marble	Junction Bed	Ham Hill Stone	Thorncombe	Brick	Cob
TARRANT CRAWFORD	ST9203	Flint	Upper Greensand	Heathstone	Purbeck	Ham Hill Stone	Brick	

Parish	NGR	Stone 1	Stone 2	Stone 3	Stone 4	Stone 5	Other 1	Other 2
TARRANT GUNVILLE	ST9212	Upper Greensand	Flint	Tisbury sandstone			Brick	Cob
TARRANT HINTON	ST9310	Flint	Upper Greensand	Tisbury sandstone			Brick	Cob
TARRANT KEYNESTON	ST9204	Flint	Upper Greensand	Heathstone			Brick	
TARRANT LAUNCESTON	ST9409	Flint	Upper Greensand				Brick	Cob
TARRANT MONKTON	ST9408	Flint	Upper Greensand				Brick	Cob
TARRANT RAWSTON	ST9306						Brick	
TARRANT RUSHTON	ST9305	Flint	Upper Greensand	Heathstone			Brick	Cob
THORNCOMBE	ST3703	Upper Greensand chert	Upper Greensand grit	Inferior Oolite				Cob
THORNFORD	ST6013	Fuller's Earth Rock	Inferior Oolite	Forest Marble				
TINCLETON	SY7791	Purbeck					Brick	
TODBER	ST8020	Corallian						
TOLLER FRATRUM	SY5797	Upper Greensand grit	Ham Hill Stone	Chalk	Forest Marble	Inferior Oolite	Flint	
TOLLER PORCORUM	SY5697	Upper Greensand grit	Chalk	Inferior Oolite	Ham Hill Stone	Flint	Brick	
TOLPUDDLE	SY7994	Purbeck	Heathstone	Flint			Brick	Cob
TRENT	ST5818	Inferior Oolite	Junction Bed	White Lias				
TURNERSPUDDLE	SY8392	Purbeck	Heathstone				Brick	Cob
TURNWORTH	ST8207	Flint	Forest Marble	Upper Greensand	Corallian		Brick	Cob
TYNEHAM	SY8880	Purbeck	Portland					
UPCERNE	ST6502	Flint					Brick	Cob
UPHALL	ST5502	Forest Marble	Flint					
UPWEY	SY6684	Purbeck						
VERWOOD	SU0808						Brick	Cob
WAREHAM	SY9287	Purbeck					Brick	Cob
WARMWELL	SY7585	Purbeck	Portland					
WEST COMPTON	SY5694	Flint	Inferior Oolite	Chalk	Upper Greensand grit			
WEST KNIGHTON	SY7387	Purbeck	Portland	Upper Greensand	Flint	Ironstone	Brick	Cob
WEST ORCHARD	ST8216	Corallian					Brick	
WEST PARLEY	SZ0897	Heathstone	Purbeck				Brick	Cob
WEST STAFFORD	SY7289	Purbeck					Brick	Cob
WEST STOUR	ST7822	Corallian						

Parish	NGR	Stone 1	Stone 2	Stone 3	Stone 4	Stone 5	Other 1	Other 2
WEYMOUTH	SY6779	Portland	Corallian	Purbeck	Bath stone		Brick	
WHITCOMBE	SY7188	Purbeck						Cob
WHITCHURCH CANONICORUM	SY3995	Inferior Oolite	Upper Greensand chert	Upper Greensand grit	Beer	Blue Lias	Brick	
WHITE LACKINGTON	SY7198	Corallian						
WIMBORNE MINSTER	SZ0099	Purbeck	Heathstone	Upper Greensand	Portland	Bath stone	Portland	
WIMBORNE ST. GILES	SU0312	Flint	Upper Greensand	Tisbury sandstone			Brick	Cob
WINFRITH NEWBURGH	SY8084	Purbeck	Portland	Flint	Heathstone		Brick	Cob
WINTERBOURNE ABBAS	SY6190	Purbeck	Flint				Brick	
WINTERBORNE CAME	SY7088	Purbeck	Portland				Brick	Cob
WINTERBORNE CLENSTON	ST8302	Flint	Upper Greensand	Portland			Brick	
WINTERBORNE HERRINGSTON	SY6888	Portland	Purbeck					
WINTERBORNE HOUGHTON	ST8204	Flint					Brick	Cob
WINTERBORNE KINGSTON	SY8697	Flint	Heathstone	Purbeck	Upper Greensand		Brick	Cob
WINTERBORNE MONKTON	SY6787	Purbeck	Flint					Cob
WINTERBORNE ST.MARTIN	SY6488	Purbeck	Flint	Heathstone	Ham Hill Stone	Upper Greensand		Cob
WINTERBORNE STEEPLETON	SY6289	Flint	Purbeck	Ham Hill Stone	Portland		Brick	
WINTERBORNE STICKLAND	ST8304	Flint					Brick	Cob
WINTERBORNE TOMSON	SY8897	Heathstone	Flint	Upper Greensand			Brick	
WINTERBORNE WHITECHURCH	ST8300	Portland					Brick	
WINTERBORNE ZELSTON	SY8997	Heathstone	Flint	Bath stone			Brick	Cob
WITCHAMPTON	ST9806	Upper Greensand	Flint	Heathstone	Purbeck	Bath stone	Brick	Cob
WOODLANDS	SU0509	Lytchett Matravers sandstone	Upper Greensand				Brick	
WOODSFORD	SY7690	Purbeck					Brick	
WOOL	SY8486	Heathstone	Purbeck					Cob
WOOLLAND	ST7707						Brick	

Parish	NGR	Stone 1	Stone 2	Stone 3	Stone 4	Stone 5	Other 1	Other 2
WOOTTON FITZPAINE	SY3795	Upper Greensand chert	Blue Lias	Inferior Oolite				Cob
WORTH MATRAVERS	SY9777	Purbeck						
WRAXALL	ST5700	Flint	Forest Marble	Chalk			Brick	
WYKE REGIS	SY6677	Purbeck	Corallian					
WYNFORD EAGLE	SY5896	Flint	Upper Greensand	Inferior Oolite	Chalk	Ham Hill Stone		
YETMINSTER	ST5910	Forest Marble	Cornbrash	Ham Hill Stone				

Parishes in which timber frame has been used.

Alderholt, Cerne Abbas, Cranborne, Durweston, Fontmell Magna, Gussage All Saints, Hampreston, Hinton St. Mary, Holt, Horton, Iwerne Minster, Okeford Fitzpaine, Pamphill, Pulham, Shapwick, Sturminster Marshall, Sturminster Newton, West Orchard, Witchampton, Woodlands.

Glossary

Anticline: an upward fold in beds of rock

Ashlar: square-cut masonry with a smooth surface and close joints

Basin: a large, low-lying area where sediment builds up over millions of years

Bedding plane: a dividing line between two layers of sedimentary rock

Bioturbation: the sediment has been disturbed by burrowing creatures or plant growth

Bivalves: a group of aquatic molluscs that have two shells or valves like mussels

Brachiopod: marine mollusc having two valves

Brackish: variable fresh to salty water

Braided river: where there are many channels and islands

Calcareous: a sedimentary rock that has calcite around the sand or shelly particles

Calcite: a mineral composed of calcium carbonate

Cement: any mineral that crystallises between particles of sediment to harden the rock

Chert: a form of quartz similar to flint, but with a fine sugary texture

Cretaceous: a unit of geological time from 140 million years ago to 65 million years ago

Cross-bedding: beds of sediment laid down at an inclined angle that is different to the angle of the beds beneath, produced by current action

Desiccation: cracks that appear in sediments on drying out under hot sun

Drift: superficial sediments deposited over solid bedrock, or as a result of deep weathering

Fault: a break that runs vertically through many layers of rock

Ferruginous: rich in iron (oxide)

Flint: a glassy form of quartz found in Chalk

Freestone: a stone that can be cut freely in any direction, often in thick beds

Gastropod: a group of molluscs with a single calcareous shell, like snails

Greensand: a sandstone with variable proportions of the green mineral glauconite (a silicate containing potassium, iron and aluminium)

Grit: a very coarse sandstone

Gypsum: hydrated calcium sulphate

Heathstone: a hard iron-rich building stone from the Tertiary heathlands

Jurassic: a unit of geological time from 205 million years ago to 140 million years ago

Laminations: thin layers of sediment usually 2-5 mm thick

Limestone: a rock composed mostly of calcium carbonate

Marble: a true marble is produced when limestone is buried deep in the earth's crust and altered by high temperatures

Marl: a soft mixture of clay and fine calcium carbonate

Micrite: a very fine-grained calcium carbonate mud

Mudstone: a fine grained sedimentary rock, including clay

Mya: million years ago

Nodule: a rounded lump of rock formed by chemical action

Oolite: a sedimentary rock consisting largely of ooliths, usually calcium carbonate

Oolith: a spherical grain that has concentric egg-shell like layers of calcium carbonate

Palaeoenvironment: the environment that existed in the geological past

Pyrite: iron sulphide (fool's gold)

Quartz: a mineral composed of silica and oxygen

RIGS: Regionally Important Geological Site

Sandstone: a rock composed mostly of sand (quartz) grains

Scarp: a steep slope formed by the edges of layers of rock that dip away in the opposite direction

Silica: silicon dioxide (SiO_2), most commonly in the form of quartz

Sparite: crystalline calcite

Strata: layers/beds of sedimentary rock

Syncline: a downward fold in beds of rock

Tertiary: a unit of geological time from 65 million years ago to 2 million years ago

Tufa: sedimentary deposit of calcium carbonate formed around springs

Unconformity: a surface indicating time gap in a sequence of sedimentary rocks

Further Reading

Note: Proceedings of the Dorset Natural History &
Archeological Society are referred to as *Dorset Proceedings*.

ANON 1829.7.13: A pillar of Purbeck stone to be erected
to Earl of Eldon. *Salisbury and Winchester Journal*,
109, 5631, p 2.

ANON 1865.8.31: Local stone from Bothenhampton used
in new church at Eype. *Dorset County Chronicle*, 12, 6,
p 111.

ANON 1866.4.26: Broadoak church at Symondsbury –
exterior walls of stone from the quarries of Stoke Abbot
near Beaminster. Gravel path edged with Eggardon
flints. *Dorset County Chronicle*, 12, 40, p 793.

ANON 1866.6.21: Broadmayne church restored – Poole
tiles in nave, Purbeck marble shafts, steps. *Dorset
County Chronicle*, 12, 48, p 949.

ANON 1866.7.12: Thornford church restored. Poole tiles
used. *Dorset County Chronicle*, 12, 51, p 1011.

ANON 1866.8.2: Okeford Fitzpaine church restored.
Portland steps to font. Purbeck marble step between
nave and chancel. *Dorset County Chronicle*, 13, 2, p 6.

ANON 1866.8.30: Wool church restored using Purbeck
marble, Poole tiles in main church and chancel floor.
Dorset County Chronicle, 13, p 5.

ANON 1866.12.6: New chancel at Poyntington church
made of Sherborne stone and Ham Hill Stone. *Dorset
County Chronicle*, 13, 20, p 7.

ANON 1867.7.25: New church at Broadwindsor. Whole
of the stone given by local landowner. *Dorset County
Chronicle*, 13, 53, p6.

ANON 1868.2.13: Piddlehinton church being restored.
Made of flint and Ridgeway stone. Red Poole tiles on
floor of nave and aisles. *Dorset County Chronicle*, 14,
29, p 12.

ANON 1868.4.23: New church at Pokeswell. Roofs
topped with Ham Hill stone. *Dorset County Chronicle*,
14, 39, p 12.

ANON 1868.8.27: Stinsford church being restored. Pillars
of Portesham stone. Window – dressings of Ham Hill
Stone. *Dorset County Chronicle*, 15, 5, p 5.

ANON 1868.9.10: New parochial school at Beaminster of
Ham Hill Stone. *Dorset County Chronicle*, 15, 7, p 8.

ANON 1869.7.8: New church at West Milton nr.
Powerstock built of local stone from Nettlecombe.
Dorset County Chronicle, 15, 50, p6.

ANON 1869.10.14: Digby Hotel in Sherborne built of
local stone and Ham Hill Stone. *Dorset County
Chronicle*, 16, 12, p 5.

ANON 1869.12.23: New church of Toller Whelme has
crosses of Ham stone, also font support. *Dorset County
Chronicle*, 16, 22, p 11.

ANON 1872.1.18: Shroton church restored. Ham Hill
Stone used for doors and windows. *Dorset County
Chronicle*, 17, 78, p 6.

ANON 1872.1.25: New church being built of local flint at
Roosdown in Lyme Regis. *Dorset County Chronicle*,
17, 79, p7.

ANON 1872.5.2: New church of St. Marks, Herston,
made of stone excavated at site, also of Purbeck,
and Purbeck stone tiles for roof. *Dorset County
Chronicle*, 17, 93, p 4.

ANON 1872.5.23: Weymouth and Dorset County Royal
Eye Infirmary built of Portland Stone. *Dorset County
Chronicle*, 17, 96.

ANON 1872.12.5: New tower at Cattistock church.
Ridgeway rock dressing, and Ridgeway stone
used. *Dorset County Chronicle*, 17, 124, p 8.

ANON 1948.6.10: Plaque of Portland stone at Brewery
memorial of 1939 – 1945 war. *Dorset County
Chronicle*, 127, 6421, p 4.

ANON 1948.11.25: Portland stone chimneys at Kingston
Maurward. *Dorset County Chronicle*, 127, 6445, p 9.

ANON 1948.12.2: Pillars in West Stafford church are of
Portland stone. *Dorset County Chronicle*, 127, 6446, p 7.

ANON 1949.3.17: Portland stone at Herringston House.
Hall is paved with Portland stone. *Dorset County
Chronicle*, 128, 6461, p 9.

ANON 1949.4.28: Piddletrenthide – font of Portland
stone. *Dorset County Chronicle*, 128, 6467, p 7.

ANON 1949.6.30: Charminster church built of local
stone – limestone and flints. *Dorset County Chronicle*,
128, 6476, p 7.

ANON 1949.8.4: 13th c font of Purbeck marble at Milton
Abbas church came from the Abbey church. *Dorset
County Chronicle*, 128, 6481, p 7.

ANON 1950.3.2: Came House built of Portland stone in
1754. *Dorset County Chronicle*, 129, 6511, p 7.

ANON 1953.10.8: River Frome diverted at Wool to go
under new bridge faced with Purbeck stone. New bridge
will be strong enough to support all the traffic. Cost
£100,000. See also 1952.3.20 for start on bridge.
Dorset County Chronicle, 132, 6699, p 3.

ANON 1957: *Quarrying building stone in Dorset.* Mining Equipment, 8 (12), 35-6.

ANON 1960: *Dorset ball clay production: two hundredth anniversary.* Refractories Journal 36 (11), 344-5.

ANON 1962: *The quarrying of Portland Stone.* Quarry Managers' Journal, 46 (6), 223-30.

ABEL F.A. 1863: *Memorandum of the results of experiments into the comparative qualities and fitness for building purposes of samples of stone from different quarries in the island of Portland.* Papers Corps of Royal Engineers, s.2, 12, 6.

ADDY S.O. & SUMMERSON J. 1933: *The evolution of the English House.* Allen and Unwin.

ALDRED M.G. 1957: *Portland quarrying.* Mine & Quarry Engineer, 23, 311-12.

ALGAR D., LIGHT A. & TREHANE P. 1979: *The Verwood & District Potteries.*

ARCHER A.A. 1972: *Sand and Gravel.* Mineral Dossier 4, Mineral Resources Consultative Committee.

ARKELL W.J. 1933: *The Jurassic System in Great Britain.* Oxford.

ARKELL W.J. 1945: The names of the strata in the Purbeck & Portland stone quarries. *Dorset Proceedings* 66, 158-68.

ARKELL W.J. 1947: The geology of the country around Weymouth, Swanage, Corfe & Lulworth. *Geological Survey Memoir UK.*

ARKELL W.J. 1947: *Oxford Stone.* Faber.

ARKELL W.J. 1950: *The future of English building stone.* Endeavour 9, 40-4.

ARKELL W.J. & TOMKEIEFF S.I. 1953: *English rock terms. Chiefly used by miners and quarrymen.* Oxford.

ATKINSON T.D. 1947: *Local style in English architecture.* Batsford.

BARKER K. 1988: Aelfric the Mass-Priest and the Anglo-Saxon Estates of Cerne Abbey. In *The Cerne Abbey Millenium Lectures.* Cerne Abbey Millenium Committee.

BARLEY M.W. 1961: *The English Farmhouse and Cottage.* Routledge and Kegan Paul.

BARTELOT R.G. 1936: *Purbeck Clay.* N & Q Somerset & Dorset, 22, 71, 67.

BARTELOT R.G. 1945: The vanished mediaeval castles of Dorset. *Dorset Proceedings* 66, 65-75.

BEAVIS J. 1971: *Some aspects of the use of Purbeck Marble in Roman Britain.* Dorset Proceedings 92, 181-204.

BEAUMONT-SLEGGE W. 1950: *Masons' marks in Dorset churches.* Dorset Proceedings 71, 73.

BENFIELD E. 1940: *Purbeck Shop. A stone workers story of stone.* Cambridge.

BERKIN L.V.I. & HOLDRIDGE D.A. 1967: Physico-chemical properties for the characterisation and control of Dorset ball clays. *Trans. Br. Ceramics Socy.* 66 (4), 189-215.

BETTEY J.H. 1972: The supply of stone for re-building St. Paul's Cathedral. *Archaeological Journal.* 128, 176-85.

BLAIR J. 1993: Purbeck Marble. In *English Medieval Industries* London, 41-56.

BLAKE J.F. 1880: The Portland building stone. *Pop. Science Review* 19, 205-212.

BOSWELL P.G.H. 1918: A memoir on British resources of sands and rocks used in glassmaking.

BOWLEY M. 1960: *Innovations in Building Materials.* Duckworth.

BRIGGS M.S. 1925: *A short history of the building crafts.* Oxford.

BRISTOW H.W. 1857: *Vertical Sections, Sheet 22,* Geological Survey. UK.

BRISTOW C.R., BARTON C.M., FRESHNEY E.C., WOOD C.J., EVANS D.J., COX B.M., IVIMEY-COOK H.C. & TAYLOR R.T. 1995: Geology of the country around Shaftesbury. *Geological Survey Memoir, UK.* Sheet 313.

BRISTOW C.R., FRESHNEY E.C. & PENN I.E. 1991: Geology of the country around Bournemouth. *Geological Survey Memoir, UK.* Sheet 32.

BROCKLEBANK J. 1979: *Victorian stone carvers in Dorset churches 1856-1880.* Dovecote Press.

BRUNSKILL R.W. 1970: *Illustrated handbook of vernacular architecture.* Faber.

BUCKMAN S.S. 1910: Certain Jurassic (Lias –Oolite) strata of south Dorset and their correlation. *Q.J. Geol. Soc. Lond,* 66, 52-89.

BUCKMAN S.S. 1925-7: *Type ammonites.* vol. 6, London.

CARTWRIGHT J.J. (ed) 1888-9: The Travels through England of Dr. Richard Pococks. *Camden Society* NS. 42 & 44.

CECIL D. 1985: *Some Dorset Country Houses.* Dovecote Press.

CLARK B.F.L. 1938: Church builders of the 19th century.

CLARK B.F.L. 1963: The building of the 18th century church. (list of 18th c benefactions in Dorset 58-9.)

CLARKE R.M. 1980: The sand and gravel resources of the country north of Bournemouth, Dorset. Resource sheet SU 00, 10, 20, SZ 09, 19, 29. *Mineral Assessment Report, Institute of Geological Sciences.* 51.

CLARKE W.B. 1838: On the phenomena exhibited by the plastic clay formation in the vicinity of Poole, Dorset. *British Association for the Advancement of Scient for 1837. Transactions of Section 93.*

CLEMENTS R.G. 1993: Type-section of the Purbeck Limestone Group, Durlston Bay, Swanage, Dorset. *Dorset Proceedings,* 114, 181-206.

CLIFTON-TAYLOR A. 1972: *The pattern of English building.* Faber.

CLIFTON-TAYLOR A. 1972: Building Materials, in Newman J. & Pevsner N. The Buildings of England, Dorset.

CLIFTON-TAYLOR A. & IRESON A.S. 1983: *English stone building.* Gollancz.

COCKBURN E.O. 1971: *The development of stone quarrying in Dorset.* MS in Dorset County Museum.

COOK O. & SMITH E. 1954: *English cottages and*

Farmhouses. Thames and Hudson.

COOK O. & SMITH E. 1968: *The English house through seven centuries*. Nelson.

COUNTRY LIFE 31.12.1948: Vanbrugh's drawings for Eastbury.

CROOK J. 1993: Winchester Cathedral 900 years.

DAMON R. 1860: *Handbook of the geology of Weymouth and the Isle of Portland*. Lond. 2nd edn. 1884.

DAVEY N. 1961: *A History of Building Materials*. Phoenix.

DEPT. OF ENVIRONMENT 1984: *Lists of buildings of special architectural or historic interest*.

DEWAR H.S.L.: Josiah Wedgwood & Dorset Clay. Ms in Dorset County Museum library.

DORSET COUNTY COUNCIL 1973: Report of ball clay working party, Russell Quay, Arne. ECC Ball Clays Ltd.

DORSET COUNTY COUNCIL, WEYMOUTH & PORTLAND B.C. & PORTLAND GROUP LTD. 1977: The stone industry on Portland.

DORSET COUNTY COUNCIL 1980: Dorset structure plan, minerals.

DORSET COUNTY COUNCIL 1982: Ball clay in Dorset.

DRAPER J. in WOODWARD P.J. 1983: The pottery in Wimborne Minster, Dorset. *Dorset Proceedings*, 105, 57-74.

DRU DRURY G. 1927: Heart burials and some Purbeck Marble heart shrines. *Dorset Proceedings*, 48, 38-58.

DRU DRURY G. 1927: First winter meeting. *Dorset Proceedings* 48, p.LVII.

DRU DRURY G. 1949: The use of Purbeck Marble in medieval times. *Dorset Proceedings* 70, 74-98.

DUGDALE G. 1948: Purbeck stone and marble. *Mercury* 1, 23.

DUNNING G.C. 1948: The Purbeck marble industry in the Roman period. *Archaeological Newsletter*, 1 (11), 14-15.

EDMUNDS F.H. & SCHAFFER R.J. 1932: Portland stone: its geology and properties as a building stone. *Proceedings of the Geologists' Association*, 43, 225-40.

ENGLISH CHINA CLAYS LTD. 1971: Information sheets on activities.

FIELD N.H. 1966: A 13th c kiln at Hermitage, Dorset. *Dorset Proceedings* 88, 161-75.

FINESSE 1981: Coade Stone. *Newsletter* 10

FISHER O. 1856: On the Purbeck strata of Dorsetshire. *Transactions of the Cambridge Philosophical Society*, ix, p.555.

FITTON W.H. 1836: Portland quarries, 1834. *Transactions of the Geological Society*. (2) iv, p.219.

FOWLER J. 1936: *Sherborne behind the seen*. Sherton Press (reprint 1986).

FOWLER J. 1938: *The stones of Sherborne Abbey*. Sherborne.

FOWLER J. 1943-46: Village sites and geological outcrops. *Somerset & Dorset Notes & Queries* 24 (195), 251; 29, 290.

FOWLER J. 1951: *Medieval Sherborne*. Longmans Dorchester.

FOWLES J. 1982: *A Short History of Lyme Regis*. Dovecote Press.

GORDON D. ST. L. 1950: Queen Anne's Men (Purbeck quarrying). *Country Life 21.07.1950*. 200.

GREEN G.W. 1998: The geology of building stone in Dorset, Hampshire & Wiltshire. *Hatcher Review*, 5 (45), 5-17.

GRINSELL L.V. 1958: *The archaeology of Wessex*. Methuen.

GRODZINSKI P. 1955: Diamond sawing revolutionizes production at Portland stone quarry. *Industrial Diamond Review* 15 (100), 199-209.

GROVES T.B. 1894: Some local stone marks. *Dorset Proceedings* 15, 168-71.

HARRISON B.P. & WILLIAMS D.F. 1979: Sherborne Old Castle, Dorset: medieval pottery fabrics. *Dorset Proceedings* 101, 91-102.

HARRISON B.P. in DUNCE J. & ROSS M.S. 1980: Pottery report, Kington Magna. *Report of Shaftesbury & District Archaeological Group 1977-80*, 22-7.

HAYSOM T. 1998: *Extracting Purbeck Marble*. Hatcher Review, 5 (45), 48-54.

HEATH S. & PRIDEAUX W.C. 1907: *Some Dorset Manor Houses*. Bemrose, London.

HIGHLEY D.E. 1975: Ball Clay. *Mineral Dossier* 11, *Mineral Resources Consultative Committee of the Institute of Geological Sciences*.

HOLDRIDGE D.A. 1959: Ball clays and their properties. *Trans. British Ceramica Socy.* 55 (6), 369-440.

HOLIDAY A. 2003: *Dorchester Building Stones*. In Coast & Country, DGAG.

HOUNSELL S.S.B. 1952: Portland and its stone. *Mine & Quarry Engineering* 18, 107-14, 143-7.

HOUSE M.R. 1989: *Geology of the Dorset Coast*. Geologists' Association Guide. 2nd edn. 1993.

HOWE J.A. 1910: *Geology of Building Stones*. Edward Arnold. Reprinted 2001.

HUDSON K. 1971: *The Fashionable Stone*. Adams & Dart, Bath. (Bath, Portland, Doulting, Clipsham, Beer et al)

HUGHES T. 2003: in Wood C. ed: *Stone roofing in England*. English Heritage Research Papers. 9, 44-53.

HUNTER W.P. 1836: Notes of a visit to the Freestone quarries of the Isle of Portland. *Mag. Natural History* 9, 97.

HUTCHINS J. 1774, 1796-1815, 1861-70. *History and antiquities of the county of Dorset*. 1st, 2nd and 3rd editions. (Has list of stone bridges in alphabetical order. Vol. 1, LXVI-LXX)

INNOCENT C.F. 1916: *The Development of English Building Construction*. Cambridge.

JERVOISE E. 1930: *The ancient bridges of the south of England*. Architectural Association.

JOINT CONSULTATIVE COMMITTEE FOR PORTLAND 1959: Ancient craft with modern mechanisation. *Bulletin Southern Regional Board for Industry* 114.

JONES I. 1993: *The Stalbridge Inheritance*. Larkwood.

JOPE E.M. 1964: The Saxon Building Industry in Southern England. *Medieval Archaeology* 8, 91-118.

KERR B. 1975: *Bound to the Soil. A social history of Dorset 1750-1918*. E.P. Publishing Ltd.

KUBALA M. 1980: The sand and gravel resources of the country around Fordingbridge, Hampshire. Resource sheet SU 11 and parts of SU 00, 01, 10, 20, & 21. *Mineral Assessment Report of the Institute of Geological Sciences*.

LANG J. 1956: *Rebuilding St. Paul's after the Fire of London*. Oxford UP.

LANG W.D. 1924: The Blue Lias of the Devon and Dorset coasts. *Proceedings of the Geologists' Association*, 35, 169-85.

LANG W.D. & PAVEY R.W.J. 1949: *Pavey Record Collection*. DRO/D447/7.

LEACH R. 1975: *An investigation into the use of Purbeck marble in medieval England*. Harrison.

LEARY E. 1983: The building limestones of the British Isles. *Building Research Establishment Report SO36*. HMSO.

LEARY E. 1986: The building sandstones of the British Isles. *Building Research Establishment Report BR84*. HMSO

LEGGE R. 1987: *Purbecks Heath, claypits, nature and the oilfield*. Dorset Publ. Co.

List of buildings of special Architectural or Historic Interest. Dept. of Environment.

LLOYD N. 1951: *A history of the English House*. Architectural Press 3rd edn.

LONG E.T. 1939: Stones in Dorset medieval churches. *Journal of the British Archaeological Assoc. n.s.* IV, 36-7.

LOWE J. 1994: *Dorset Building Materials Survey. A pilot project*. Dorset County Council.

MACHIN R. 1978: *The houses of Yetminster*. Univ. Bristol Extra Mural Dept.

MACHIN R. 1983: *The building accounts of Mapperton Rectory 1699-1701*. Dorset Record Soc.

MATHERS S.J. 1982: The sand and gravel resources of the country between Dorchester and Wareham, Dorset. Resource sheets comprising parts of ST 68, 69, 78, 79, 88, 89, 98, 99. *Mineral Assessment Report of the Institute of Geological Sciences*. 103.

MELVILLE R.V. & FRESHNEY E.C. 1982: The Hampshire Basin. *British Regional Geology*. 4th edn.

MOOREHEAD 1887: Abbotsbury iron ore. *Dorset Proceedings*, 8, XLIV.

MUSTY J. 1961: The Laverstock Pottery. *Museums Journal* 60, 251-5.

MUSTY J., ALGAR D. & EWENCE P.F. 1969: Medieval pottery kilns at Laverstock. *Archaeologica*, 102, 83-150.

NEWMAN J. & PEVSNER N. 1972: *The buildings of England. Dorset*. Penguin. 2nd edn 1985.

OLIVER B. 1929: *The cottages of England; a review of their types and features from the 16th to the 18th centuries*. Batsford.

OSWALD A. 1953: Country houses of Dorset. *Country Life*. 1935.

PARSONS D. 1990: *Stone. Quarrying & Building in England AD 43-1525*. Phillimore.

PERKINS J.W. et al 1979: *Bath Stone, a quarry history*. University College, Cardiff.

PENTIN H. 1916: Old Portland. *Dorset Proceedings* 37, 228-53.

PERCY J. 1865: Metallurgy. 2 Dorset iron ore.

PICKERING K.T. 1995: Are enigmatic sandy wave-like bedforms in Jurassic Bridport Sands, Dorset due to standing waves? *Journal of the Geological Society of London*. 152, 481-5.

PIKE BROS., FAYLE & CO. 1964: Catalogue of Dorset Ball clays. Wareham.

POPE A. 1927: Photographs of some ancient stone bridges in Dorset. *Dorset Proceedings*, 48, LV-LVII.

PROCEEDINGS 1931, 1902: *Dorset Proceedings*.

RANSOME T. & COOPER B. 1848: On the composition of some of the limestones used for building purposes, especially on those employed in the erection of the new Houses of Parliament. *Mem. Geol. Surv. UK* 2 (2), 685-91.

RICHARDSON L.F. 1927-30: Inferior Oolite & contiguous deposits in Burton Bradstock - Broadwindsor district; and Sherborne district. *Proceedings of the Cotteswold Club* 23, 35-68, 149-85, 253-63 & 24, 35-85.

RICHARDSON N.M. 1893: *Dorset Proceedings*, 14.

RICHARDSON N.M. 1894: *Dorset Proceedings*, 15.

RICHARDSON N.M. 1922: The travels of Peter Mundy in Dorset in 1635. *Dorset Proceedings*, 42, 44.

ROSS M.S. 1986: Kington Magna.

ROYAL COMMISSION ON HISTORICAL MONUMENTS 'Inventories of Dorset: Vol. 1: West Dorset (1952), Vol. 2: South East Dorset (1970), Vol. 3: Central Dorset (1970), Vol. 4: North Dorset (1972), Vol. 5: East Dorset (1975)'.

RUDLER F.W. 1893: Handbook to the collection of British Pottery and Porcelain in the Museum of Practical Geology, London.

SALTER A.E. 1898: Pebbly and other gravels in southern England. *Proceedings of the Geologists' Association* 15, 264.

SALZMAN L.F. 1923: *English Industries of the Middle*

Ages. Oxford. 1964.

SALZMAN L.F. 1967: *Building in England down to 1540. A Documentary History*. Oxford. 1952.

SANCTUARY M. 1956: *This was my village*. DRO/768/1.

SCHAFFER R.J. 1932: The weathering of natural building stones. *Sp. Report* 18, Building Research, Dept. Sci. & Indust. Research HMSO.

SCOTT A. 1929: The Dorset deposits and clayworks. *Sp. Rep. Mineral Resources GB*. 31, Ball Clay, 37-41.

SHIPP W., HODSON J.W. & HOWEL 1861: Purbeck sections or quarrying terms. In Hutchins, vol. 1, 685-7.

SMEATON 1791: Eddystone Lighthouse. 62 et seq.

SMITH C.H. 1840: Lithology, or observations on stone used for building (Portland). *Royal Institute of British Architects*, 129.

SMITH M.R. ed 1999: Stone: Building stone, rock fill and armourstone in construction. App. C Properties of some British building stones. *Geol.Soc.Sp.Publ.* 16.

SOUTH WESTERN STONE CO. LTD. 1959: Stone for building.

STONE FIRMS LTD. 1962: Stone and the architect.

STRAHAN A. 1898: The geology of the Isle of Purbeck and Weymouth. *Geological Survey Memoir, UK*.

SYDENHAM J. 1839: History of the town and county of Poole.

THOMAS J. 1989: An unexpected foundation stone. *Dorset Proceedings*, 110, 168.

THOMAS J. 1990: The lesser-known building materials of West Dorset. *Proceedings of the Geologists' Association*, 101 (4), 289-301.

THOMAS J. 1993: The Building Stones of Dorset. Part 1. The Western parishes - Upper Greensand Chert & Lower Lias. *Dorset Proceedings*, 114, 161-8.

THOMAS J. 1994: The Building Stones of Dorset. Part 2. Chideock to Broadwindsor. Middle and Upper Lias. *Dorset Proceedings*, 115, 133-8.

THOMAS J. 1995: The Building Stones of Dorset. Part 3. Inferior Oolite, Forest Marble, Cornbrash and Corallian Limestones. The parishes inland of the Chesil Bank. Bothenhampton to Chickerell. *Dorset Proceedings*, 116, 61-70.

THOMAS J. 1996: The Building Stones of Dorset. Part 4. The northern parishes which use Forest Marble and Cornbrash limestones. *Dorset Proceedings*, 117, 95-100.

THOMAS J. 1998: *Stone Quarrying*. Dovecote Press, Discover Dorset series.

THOMAS J. 2003: *Cerne Abbas*. In Coast & Country. DGAG.

THOMAS J. 2003: *Sherborne Building Stones*. In Coast & Country. DGAG.

THOMAS J. & ENSOM P.C. 1989: *A Bibliography and Index of the geology of Dorset*. Dorset Natural History & Archaeological Society.

TORRENS H.S. 1975: The coal seekers, or coal exploration in Dorset. *Dorset* 44.

TORRENS H.S. 1979: William Sharpe, 1724-83 and coal in Dorset. *N. & Q. Somerset and Dorset* 30 (14), 33.

TREDGOLD T. 1820: An account of some experiments on the flexibility and strength of stones. *Philosophical Magazine*, 56, 290.

TREVES F. 1906: *Highways and byways in Dorset*. Macmillan.

TUCKER M.E. 1992: *Sedimentary Petrology*. Blackwell.

TURNOR R. 1952: *The smaller English house, 1500 to 1939*. Batsford.

VICTORIA COUNTY HISTORY OF THE COUNTIES OF ENGLAND; DORSET. 1908.

WADHAM A.W. 1994: *Building Stones of Southampton*. Southampton Geology Field Study Group.

WAITE A.G. 1971: *The development of stone quarrying in Dorset*. MS in Dorset County Museum.

WALLIS A.J. 1974: *Dorset Bridges*. Sherborne, The Abbey Press.

WALLIS A.M. 1891: The Portland stone quarries. *Dorset Proceedings* 12, 187-94.

WALLIS A.M. 1898: In Strahan, A Geology of Purbeck & Weymouth. *Geological Survey Memoir*,. UK.

WARNES A. 1926; *Building stones: their properties, decay and preservation*. Benn.

WARREN F.C. 1938: Dorset industries in the past. *Dorset Proceedings* 59, 32-46.

WARREN F.C. 1951: Dorset livelihoods. *Dorset Year Book 1951-2*, 133-45.

WATSON J. 1911: *British and Foreign building stones*. Cambridge.

WEBSTER T. 1826: Observations on the Purbeck and Portland Beds. *Transactions of the Geological Society* (2), ii, p.38-9.

WHITE H.J.O. 1917: The geology of the country around Bournemouth. Sheet 329. 2nd edn. *Geological Survey Memoir, UK*.

WILLIAMS-ELLIS C. & EASTWICK-FIELD J. 1947: *Building in cob, pise and stabilized earth*. Country Life, rev. edn.

WILSON V., WELCH F.B.A., ROBBIE J.A. & GREEN G.W. 1958: Geology of the country around Bridport & Yeovil. *Geological Survey Memoir, UK*.

WOOD M. 1965: *The English medieval house*. Phoenix.

WOODWARD H.B. 1895: Jurassic Rocks of Britain. vol. v. *Geological Survey Memoir, UK*.

WRIGHT J.K. 1981: The Corallian rocks of North Dorset. *Proceedings of the Geologists' Association*, 92, 17-32.

WRIGHT J.K. 1986: A new look at the stratigraphy, sedimentology and ammonite fauna of the Corallian Group (Oxfordian) of south Dorset. *Proceedings of the Geologists' Association*, 97, (1), 1-21.

YOUNG D. 1968: Brickmaking at Broadmayne. *Dorset Proceedings*, 89, 318-24.

YOUNG D. 1972: Brickmaking in Dorset. *Dorset Proceedings*, 93, 213-42.

YOUNG D. 1979: The Verwood potteries. *Dorset Proceedings*, 101, 103-20.

Acknowledgements

My grateful thanks for assistance in many and varied ways are due to:

Jane Clarke, who redrew the diagrams.

Jon Corkill, the Geographical Information Systems officer of the Dorset Environmental Records Centre, who has translated my records of pits and quarries, and the use of different building stones in the parishes, into clear and meaningful maps. We have not used the British Geological Survey colours for the building stones partly because they have changed them over the past ten years and partly because we wished to show the different Formations in distinctive colours. On the British Geological Survey maps several important limestones are delineated in very similar colours.

The Jurassic Coast World Heritage Site Team, who paid for Jon Corkill's time in creating the maps for the book.

The late Miss Pamela Cunnington, Historic Buildings Officer of the Dorset County Council for many years, who drew up a map showing the proportion of stone, brick, cob and timber frame used in each of the parishes. Her information on brick, cob and timber frame is included in the final chapter, Building Stone by Parish.

Members of the Dorset group of the Geologists' Association who have helped me identify stone in their particular area of expertise.

Hugh Jaques and the staff of the Dorset History Centre for assistance with researching the maps and records of quarrying.

Paul Ensom, who has the foresight to encourage amateurs to pursue their individual interests and thereby add to the store of geological knowledge.

The Geologists' Association Curry Fund who provided initial funding to start the research.

Trev Haysom, Kevin Keates and other quarrymen for their expertise.

John Lowe, the current Historic Buildings Officer of the Dorset County Council, who organised the pilot study of building materials on behalf of English Heritage.

Pete Zapadka, whose website on the Mason-Dixon Line in Maryland, U.S.A., proved so informative.

The many farmers, landowners, architects, bridge engineers and long term residents of Dorset who have kindly shared their knowledge of rural Dorset.

The photographs were a joint effort between myself and my husband Mike Thomas, except for Adrian Cooper, page 12; David Bailey, Front cover, pages 2/3, 32 (bottom); Dovecote Press, Back cover, 102 (bottom), 107 (top).

Index